Once Upon A Totem

Totem poles

stand today in parks and museums in such far-flung places as New York, Toronto, London, Paris; in all of them unquestioned aliens. In only one area are they at home: on the wild strip of land stretching along the North Pacific Coast from Alaska to Oregon. Here they belong to history, monuments to a people who wore no feathered war bonnets, moved no tepees, rode no pinto ponies.

Instead these people rode the oceans in swift canoes, feasted at sumptuous potlatches, and lived in great cedar lodges. Fed bountifully by sea and land, they had ample time to carve their poles with symbols of their past, and tell the stories that went with the symbols.

All five stories told here are rich in the mythology and historic grandeur of these people. But the stories are more than this; they are exciting tales that illustrate again, as all great myths and legends do, the qualities of courage, nobility of character, strength of purpose, and gentleness of spirit that great people share.

Christie Harris

ONCE UPON
A TOTEM

Woodcuts by John Frazer Mills

Atheneum New York

1967

TO MY SONS AND DAUGHTERS:

Michael, Moira, Sheilagh, Brian, AND *Gerald Harris,*

ALL CHILDREN OF THE THUNDERBIRD COAST

Preface

TOTEM POLES stand in parks and museums around the world. They tower in such widespread cities as New York, Toronto, London, Paris, Berlin, and Edinburgh, grotesquely alien.

Only in one area are they at home. This is the wild strip of land stretching along the North Pacific coast from Alaska to Oregon. Here totem poles belong, shrouded in soft mist against the green of rain forests and the blue of rugged snow-capped mountains.

Here they belong to history, monuments to a people unique among the Indians of North and South America: Indians who wore no feathered war bonnets; who moved no easy tepees; who rode no pinto ponies.

The totems which these Indians of the North Pacific flaunted on their belongings were figures drawn from the legendary history of their tribe and family. Strictly speaking, they were not totems, for most real totems were animals thought to have been the ancestors of the clans which bore their names. Here they were merely emblems, recalling old tribal stories. They were cherished, though, as inherited possessions. Their use was jealously restricted.

Native artists depicted such characters as Thunderbird, Wolf, Killer-Whale, Raven, and Grizzly Bear on large rectangular cedar houses which were the best Indian lodges on the continent. They carved or painted them, too, on graceful canoes, storage chests, horn spoons, earrings, and war clubs, as well as on the heraldic columns we know as totem poles. These figures were the proud symbols of their great clans, or phratries, and of their smaller family groups. These were their coats-of-arms, won mainly by adventure.

"Vikings of the North Pacific," the more daring northern tribes have been called, for their swift dugout canoes sliced through sea swells on slave raids as far south as California. They roved the coast, hunted on land and sea, and fished the rivers.

"People of the Potlatch," they have all been called, for their great potlatch gatherings were the heart of a complex social system. Having no written language to use on records, they found it practical to conduct their affairs in public. Claims to the ownership of such property as salmon streams and clam beaches; of such non-material wealth as crests, dances, legends, songs, and ceremonies; and of a clan's hereditary high-ranking names, all had to be witnessed, not only by members of the kinship group involved, but also by important people from other clans and tribes. This was done at a potlatch.

Mainly for the prestige of the host, guests had to be lavishly feasted and entertained. They had to be presented with gifts, also, for their service as witnesses. Since the gifts would be returned later, however, with interest, the potlatch tended to serve as a bank and insurance company as well as a court and festival of the arts.

Isolated by wild mountains and fed by the bounty of sea and river, the unchallenged lords of the coast had ample leisure to develop rich artistic talents. Potlatch display provided a strong incentive. Greatest in the arts were the bold northern nations. Haida, Tsimshian, Tlingit, and Kwakiutl especially enriched their lives with painting and sculpture, song and dance, story and ceremonial. Adventures of their ancestors supplied them with their motifs.

Often the heroes of these adventures seemed to have come, as they themselves had come, out of the ancient Old World; mythical heroes who, like themselves, had taken on the New World colors of salmon and cedar, sea otter and painted totem.

Five of their tales inspired *Once Upon a Totem*.

Contents

Once Upon A Totem

One

A TOTEM POLE was usually raised to honor a particular chief, living or dead. It carried every crest he was entitled to use: his clan totem, his family emblems, and his personal coat-of-arms. It might also include his wife's totems to make it more impressive.

When the pole was raised with much ceremony at a potlatch, the story behind each crest was dramatically recounted. Customarily, each story told how one of the symbols came to be the emblem of a mythical ancestor and the property of his heirs.

Such a tale is "The One-Horned Mountain Goat."

It tells how Du'as, a stripling hunter, won the Mountain Goat emblem for himself and his descendants. It demonstrates why each figure on a totem pole was a potent image, as meaningful and inspiring to the one who owned it as was a coat-of-arms to a knight.

Du'as belonged to the great clan that had Killer Whale and Bear as its chief symbols. Like all northwest natives, he lived in a gigantic cedar house decorated with his ancestral totems. He had his hereditary crests tattooed on his body, also, and painted or carved on all the things he used. Though unable to read or write, he was a proud and cultured boy.

4

The setting for this ancient myth is Temlaham, the Tsimshian Garden of Eden on the banks of the Ksan River; a place now known as the Hazelton country on the Skeena River.

The One Horned Mountain Goat

LONG, LONG AGO there lived an Indian boy, Du'as, who found one northern summer almost endless. It seemed to him that the golden tints of autumn would never brighten the aspen trees along the lower slopes of Stek-yaw-den.

Every morning, day after day, he leapt up from his sleeping platform, rushed out of doors, and looked toward the mountain, hoping to find the leaves changed. This would be Stek-yaw-den's signal, its sign that the time had come, at last, to prepare for the great fall goat hunt. And this year. Du'as would be among the tribal hunters.

Impatiently he watched, and watched, and waited. And then finally it came. One day there was no doubt. The green leaves were tinged with yellow.

In sheer delight Du'as climbed a small pine and rocked it. Then, with a joyous whoop, he raced back to the Killer Whale House, darting in through the hole cut in his family's crest pole. Now, at long last, the traditional hunt rituals would begin, and this time Du'as would be part of them. His heart sang like a merry bird. And it kept on singing right through the lengthy, solemn rites that preceded the year's chief goat hunt.

When these rites had been accomplished, the day came to go off to the hunting lodges. Suppressing an urge to leap and shout, Du'as stood waiting for his leader's whistle.

Like Du'as, the whole village surged with eagerness; although unlike him, few people stood still. Men checked on spears; women ducked in and out of houses; canoes strained at their anchor stones. The air itself seemed to stir in preparation.

Only one man appeared unmoved. Du'as's grandfather, a famous totem carver, chipped calmly at a fragrant cedar log with his adze. Du'as could not understand this. The day was so very special.

Taut as a drawn bowstring, he waited and he watched the waiting hills. Suddenly his eye caught a movement of white across a rock outcropping. Then a great white buck leapt high on a crag that overlooked the valley and stood in proud majesty.

"The Chief of the goats," he breathed in awe and turned to Katla, his little sister. "The Chief himself is watching for my coming," he joked. Although he laughed, his eyes shone with a secret hope. Perhaps on his first hunt he would drop that goat. It haunted the dreams of many, he knew, but perhaps, perhaps, it would be his. He glanced at the provision bags he meant to fill for winter.

"You will grow fat," he promised Katla, pinching her lean brown shoulder. "You'll greet the spring-time fat and saucy as any robin."

"So will the mountain goats," scoffed his grandfather. "Boasting fills few food boxes." Carefully the old man measured the housepost he was carving.

"You have prepared yourself with proper fasting?" the carver asked. "And bathed, Du'as? And drunk the juice of Devil's Club for power?"

"Of course I have, Grandfather." What hunter would neglect the rites that nimbled his feet and strengthened his hunting magic?

"And you will remember the sacred laws of life when you have killed the white goats?"

The boy's eyes lost their shine at this stern question. Those old laws about the goats! Grandfather could never understand how hard they were to keep, these days.

"You will remember the Sky Chief's laws of life?" insisted the boy's grandfather.

"I . . . I will remember," Du'as replied. He would

willingly observe the basic laws, but would he dare perform the old fashioned rituals that went with them? Others, he knew, would scoff. "I will remember," he said again, his voice dulled by the grudging promise.

"Remember what?" another voice asked lightly.

Du'as whirled to face his prince, Wi-ho-om. The eyes of the boy rested respectfully on the man's dark chest, for tattooed there was Thunderbird, one of the sacred symbols. This showed Wi-ho-om's descent straight from the Sky Chief himself, down through the ancient line of royal mothers.

"You will remember what?" the prince insisted. His dark eyes glinted with his teasing. "That goats are very safe from our young Du'as?" He tossed the boy a careless grin before moving along to join three royal comrades. Princes, like him, each wore a sacred emblem: Moon, Star, or Rainbow, the sign of a Sky ancestor.

"They are great hunters," Du'as said proudly, admiring his royal clansmen.

"And foolish men," his grandfather retorted promptly. "With no respect for lesser living creatures. Calamity will come," he added darkly.

The boy winced at the word *calamity*. It had become a joke among the hunters. They called Grandfather "Old Calamity." They laughed about his fears of dire disaster.

"Calamity will come," warned his grandfather.

"Is Calamity an ogre?" Katla asked him.

Du'as just laughed and tweaked a braid, tinkling

its pretty seashells. Uneasy now, and anxious to be gone, he picked up his horn-tipped climbing staff; he slung on his bow and quiver. This talk about old laws made him feel embarrassed.

A cedar whistle shrilled.

"Off to the hunting huts!" sang out Wi-ho-om.

Du'as sprang gratefully toward the river. The time for the hunt had come. He would forget the vague fears that were spoiling his perfect morning.

Across the river, packers moved out with bags and sleeping mats, with snowshoes and camp provisions. They headed for steep Stek-yaw-den.

Du'as's spirits rose. Goat hunting was the height of all adventure. And who could tell? Perhaps he would take the great white buck on his first foray. Men said this buck was as proud as a Thunderbird and as white as a moonlit birch tree. And perhaps it would be his.

Hunting high in the hills, day after day, the boy's joy knew no bounds. It was all he had hoped it would be. He bounded with the agile goats; he soared with the mountain eagles. And golden days swept by like the fleeting leaves of autumn. Du'as scaled rocky cliffs, leapt breathless chasms, and sent his arrows singing. He kept watch over cunning pits. Few goats were his alone, though he helped corner many for older hunters. Those that were his own, he accorded a skimpy ritual, performing it in secret caves while he seethed with resentment toward his stern grandfather.

"These worn out old goat rites!" he muttered darkly. The goat laws themselves were fine, but he hated having to hide old rituals.

He soon forgot his annoyance, though, in dreaming about the goats' Chief. But to him, and to every other hunter, the elusive buck remained only a teasing white flash, a challenge that sharpened their instincts.

Then, too soon, provision bags were filled to over-flowing with good dried strips of meat and kidney fat. Black mounds of horns rose beside the hunting huts, ready to be carved into spoons or used as grips on mountain staffs and snowshoes. Goatskins lay waiting for men to carry them down the rough slopes.

Yet the great white buck was safely hidden, defeating even the princes' efforts to outwit him.

"We must go home," Du'as commented, sighing.

"Without that buck?" Wi-ho-om scoffed. "And know ourselves outsmarted by a goat? No, my young clansman, I've sworn to take that buck's head as a trophy."

"A trophy?" Du'as gasped. Surely Wi-ho-om joked? Such disrespect to a goat would break all laws. The hunter's code allowed killing for human needs, but never killing for vanity. He glanced at the provision bags and packing boxes. There was enough meat in them now for even the grimmest winter. So there must be no more killing. "The . . . the old laws of life!" he stammered, still shocked, and not quite believing.

Fierce as the Thunderbird was Wi-ho-om's reply. "The old laws are old," he snapped, "and like old trees they must fall and be forgotten." He tossed away a bone with good meat on it.

Startled at this, Du'as remembered his grandfather's warning. Calamity came when people grew brash and careless; when they failed in respect to living creatures. He flushed with shame, recalling his own grudging rituals.

"You will remember the Sky Chief's laws of life?" Du'as seemed to hear the old man's voice again, echoing through the mountains. He recounted those laws in silence: goat meat should not be wasted, nor bones tossed off where greedy wolves might gnaw them; the bones and scraps should all be neatly piled and reverently burned, as human remains were, to free the spirit selves for happy rebirth. The goats would be angry if these laws were dishonored. They might disappear. Calamity indeed might come to the Temlaham people.

Du'as felt a hand fall on his shoulder, interrupting his troubled thoughts.

"Don't think of old men's tales," Wi-ho-om ordered. "Change with the times, young Killer Whale."

"But . . ." Du'as fell silent. Were they old tales? Or were the ancient laws the way of wisdom? Was Grandfather lost in a world as ancient as his totems? Or were old laws, like totems, everlasting?

"Come, Du'as," Wi-ho-om urged, "we hunt once more. And this time we will take the goats' great Chief. I will not rest if that old buck defeats me. Besides, you need the training, for I mean to make a hunter of you."

Flattered, though still uneasy, Du'as went out again along the goat trails. With other hunters, he scoured rugged slopes, leapt treacherous canyons, and blocked narrow passes. It was a long hunt, but they kept on until, at last, the Chief of the goats was cornered. Caught in a towering dead end, the mighty beast whirled to stand at bay.

"Yi-eeee!" Exhilarated by the chase, Du'as cried out for joy; but, as the great beast turned to face him, as proud as a Thunderbird and as white as a moonlit

birch tree, his triumph ended. He opened his mouth to shout some word of protest, but a spear flashed by him.

The great white buck fell. His eyes blazed once more, then dulled forever.

Du'as could have wept had he not been so angry. This noble beast should have died for a more worthy purpose. "We do not need his meat," he said, defiantly.

Wi-ho-om merely scoffed. "Who hunts for meat today? This is for glory. I'll take just his head to show the tribe." Careless and full of boasts, he hacked the proud head off, leaving the carcass for the wolves to plunder.

Later, he hoisted the trophy high on his spear and, swaggering, led the hunting party back to the ancient village. He laughed at people who showed alarm. "Change with the times," he told them.

"Calamity will come," the old carver muttered. He turned his piercing eyes to his grandson. "You kept the sacred laws?" he sternly asked.

"I . . . I tried," said Du'as. He twisted one foot beneath him.

"Then you are kind and brave. A worthy hunter."

The boy's dark features flushed. He was ashamed of how he had helped Wi-ho-om; even more ashamed of how he had skimped old rituals, performing them in secret. He was kind and brave? His grudging observance had had little of kindness in it, and little of courage, either. Kind? Brave? Du'as cringed inside and avoided the carver's glances.

Sensing that his thoughts were troubled, Katla

slipped her hand in his. "You are a great hunter," she assured her brother. "Look at the food you've brought for winter. I think I will greet the springtime as fat and saucy as any robin."

"You may need sauciness to greet a hungry springtime," said the old carver sternly.

"Let's talk about the feasts," suggested Katla, disregarding the grim prediction. Patting the hunting bags with her small fingers, she chattered of plans the villagers were making.

Du'as listened eagerly. Potlatch time was a time he loved, a time for songs and dances and stories around the lodgefire. People were coming to Temlaham. They had been invited many moons before. Guests would be lodged, each with his own clan kinsmen: Ravens with Ravens, Eagles with Eagles, Wolves with Wolves.

A hunter now, Du'as looked forward to sharing the feastlodge hosting. He would dress in clan regalia and dance with the other hunters. His eyes began to sparkle with the prospect. But his joy was short lived; for even as they talked, Wi-ho-om tossed his prized trophy to a group of children.

"Dance with the old goat, boys," he shouted gayly. And the brash children did, wearing it like a dance mask. They pulled its beard; they kicked at the boy who wore it.

A few shocked people hid their eyes in horror. "Such ridicule!" they cried. "Such an insult invites ghost-vengeance from the goat tribe."

Du'as, as he watched in alarm, seemed to feel the

great buck's spirit self looking down upon the clowning children. The buck was angry, he felt sure, and with sufficient reason. He himself was so full of anger he could scarcely contain it.

"Calamity will come," said the old carver. "When hunting comes again, before the time of leafing, you will find no goats up there. Your pits will be empty, like your bellies."

Most people laughed at him and went on with their potlatch planning. Du'as, putting his fears away, practiced the ancient clan dances and preened himself in his Killer Whale regalia.

When the feast time came, however, and the drums were throbbing wildly, he found that only his feet were dancing. His heart hung heavy and his mind was troubled. The old buck haunted him. Surely revenge would follow Wi-ho-om's insults. As Grandfather had so often warned, the goat tribe might leave Stek-yaw-den.

But it did not. When the feasting was over, when winter's worst storms were finished, when the leaf buds were gently swelling, hunters found the customary plenty on the mountain. Goats fell into their pits as they had always fallen, and every bag was filled to overflowing.

"You see," Wi-ho-om scoffed to his young clansman, "the goats are powerless against my power!" He swelled his chest to flaunt his sacred symbol. Then he led his hunters on the trails again. Just for the sport of it they ranged, killing and wounding many. They left the dead for slinking wolves to plunder.

Du'as felt sick at heart to see such wanton killing. His ancestors had lived and died as hunters, but they had loved wild creatures. They had kept the ancient laws with pride and vigor.

"The Sky Chief's laws of life . . ." he dared to remind the others as they finally started homeward.

"Are old," Wi-ho-om snapped, "and like old trees they must fall and be forgotten."

"But . . . we . . . should not be selfish," Du'as ventured.

"You're right," Wi-ho-om replied with sudden gusto. He swooped up a snow white goat kid from a thicket. "I'll take this to my children."

"A kid?" gasped Du'as, almost unbelieving. That was the strictest law of all: respect for the young of creatures. Wi-ho-om could not mean it!

Unabashed by Du'as's startled face, the prince took the goat kid home. There he flung it to a group of high born children. "Here, have some sport," he urged them, laughing lightly.

"Let's see if it can swim," a boy suggested. He jerked a thumb toward the icy river.

Du'as walked away. He could not bear to watch. Yet he dared not protest again. He strolled along the river bank and finally stood watching the water's rush, his shoulders slumping.

There Katla found him.

"Du'as," she panted. She grabbed his reluctant fingers. "Oh, Du'as, come and stop them!" She caught her breath, then cried with indignation, "They'll kill that baby goat if you don't stop them!"

Du'as squatted down before his little sister. He laid his big hands on her heaving shoulders. "I can not help you, Katla," he said, grimly.

She shook off angry tears. "You have to stop them, Du'as."

"I can't," he insisted, but his eyes narrowed and glinted as she sobbed out her story:

"Oh Du'as, they . . . they threw him in the river to . . . to see if he could swim . . . and . . . when he struggled out, they threw him in again. Then when he got too shivery, they threw him in the fire . . . to warm him up, they said." The child's eyes blazed with anger. "Then when his wool was burning, they tossed him in the river . . . to cool him off, they said. He'll die! He'll die! Oh, Du'as, come and stop them!"

"I can't," her brother answered.

"Then you're not kind and brave," she stormed, whirling back toward the cruel children.

Shamed by the taunt, Du'as followed his little sister; and, seeing the tiny kid half burned, half frozen, he could stand no more. His pent up anger burst forth. He toppled small children; he sent their elders spinning. Katla, too, moved in like an avenging whirlwind. Little princes found themselves struggling out of the icy river. Small nobles picked themselves up from startlingly hot cinders. Royal noses bled, streaming crimson across proud emblems.

Du'as snatched up the goat kid and ran toward his

grandfather, who was waiting with oolaken ointment ready.

The old man soothed the small goat's burns with his mixture of red ochre, herbs, and oolaken fish grease. Katla ran for her warmest rabbitskin to wrap around the shivering baby. Then the three of them moved off toward Stek-yaw-den.

When the kid seemed strong enough, they set it down and urged it gently homeward.

"Go, little friend," said Du'as. "Go, and forgive us."

"Calamity will come," warned his grandfather.

"To us," Du'as agreed. "To me, especially, for defying great Prince Wi-ho-om."

"To the whole village," insisted the old man darkly.

But both were wrong. The prince said nothing, ashamed perhaps, down in his secret spirit; and nothing evil happened to the village. The fish came up the river as they had always come. The red strawberries sweetened. Pink roses bloomed and filled the air with fragrance. Lupin, daisies, and paintbrush spread their lovely carpets; and shimmering days flowed by.

"You see?" Wi-ho-om scoffed to the old carver.

"I see. And you will see, Wi-ho-om."

"I will see you laughed at for your dismal howlings. Go with the wolves, old man, and swell their nightly chorus."

It was after the Moon of Berries and before the great fall hunt that a strange thing happened. It started with the sound of cedar whistles and cedar bugles, coming on the wind from blue Stek-yaw-den.

"More invitations to more feasts," chirped Katla. Her brown eyes sparkled with anticipation.

"That cannot be," objected her grandfather. "The messengers have long ago brought all the invitations." His piercing eyes searched questioningly among the aspen trees. "Besides, Katla, there is no tribe on Stek-yaw-den to send an invitation."

Four messengers appeared, however, coming straight from the mountain. Their faces were painted red and white, as was the proper custom. They wore the proper twisted-red-cedar bands around their heads, topped by black raven feathers. Their cloaks were of mountain goatskin.

"Men from Stek-yaw-den?" Du'as asked, frowning and watching closely. He felt an odd foreboding. He remembered strange tales of ancient days, when things had been much different; when animals had taken human form at times, to avenge themselves on people. "Men from Stek-yaw-den?" he muttered, a question in his voice.

"Pffff! Some new migration," people suggested. Had not most of the clans arrived by old migrations? Why not a new one? At least these people came the way they should when bringing an invitation. They were obviously a proper folk, with excellent formal manners. "They must not be slighted, either," many Temlahams cautioned Du'as.

Only the boy and his grandfather seemed to feel uneasy. Others went happily out to welcome the visitors. Men paddled across to meet them. Women brought smoked salmon and oolaken fish grease. Chiefs donned totem headdresses and handsome, fringed, patterned mantles: they picked up their carved-bird rattles and danced in formal welcome, scattering white eagle down, the sacred pledge of peace.

"Greetings to the high chiefs!" the four strangers hailed the dancers. In flowing oratory they offered an invitation. Their own high chief, they said, The-Great-One-of-the-Hills, wanted to feast the people of this village. He wanted to show them his wealth and power, and he wished them to come at once, before the snow fell.

With formal dignity, the Temlaham chiefs accepted. Although this was unusual, they agreed that their people would start the next morning.

"Go to Stek-yaw-den?" Du'as's grandfather muttered. His wise old eyes surveyed the messengers.

"Why do you look so glum?" Wi-ho-om asked him.

"Because of what will happen," said the carver. "These men are not true men."

"How would you know?" Wi-ho-om sneered. "You see through a fog of foolish fear, old carver."

"Calamity will come," the old man answered.

"Go with the wolves! Howl with their nightly chorus!" Wi-ho-om swelled his chest. Nothing could harm the Sky Chief's descendent, he seemed to boast. Nothing could touch a prince who wore the Thunderbird, symbol of sacred power.

Next morning when the tribe was leaving, gay with anticipation, the old man picked up his adze and started chipping.

"You really will not go?" asked Du'as, frowning. Of course, others were staying, too; but only the very old, and the very young and their watchful mothers. Their failure to go could not be thought an insult to the new neighbors.

"And I'm not going, too," said little Katla. Her eyes were sad with disappointment.

"And you, Du'as?" the carver asked. He looked at his grandson sharply.

"I cannot slight The-Great-One-of-the-Hills," the boy answered simply. "I have to go."

"You have to go," agreed the old man, sadly.

So Du'as went.

A haze was on the hills, making them deeply blue. A breeze rippled the grasses; it stirred the glistening poplars. Moving through such a world, Du'as found his heart grow gay as a goldenrod. Fears lifted like mist, and he climbed the slopes with rising joy.

"These are not true men?" Wi-ho-om said nudging him when they could see the feasthouse. The building was fine indeed, edging a sheer rock cliff and half-circled by blue-green spruce trees.

"They must have brought split cedar and house-poles with them," Du'as noted with eager interest. Perhaps this was a great new clan, with many slaves, and sharper tools than the Temlahams had to work with. Their carving was very good, though it depicted a strange clan totem. Instead of a familiar Eagle or Wolf or Bear, it presented a Mountain Goat crest.

"These people are surely migrants," the Temlahams told each other. "No Raven House, no Killer Whale House, only this Mountain Goat House." They found comforting reassurance, however, in the familiar courteous customs. Women came forth with crabapples and nuts and berries; chiefs came shaking their rattles and dancing in full regalia. To Du'as it seemed fine indeed, although he had a strange feeling that something was missing.

Inside the huge feasthouse, the drums were throbbing. Bright flames rose, licking toward the smokehole; they flickered on houseposts carved with the strange Goat totem.

"Not proper men?" Wi-ho-om scoffed to Du'as. Then he strode to the rear to take his honored place. His cloak of sea-otter skins gleamed black as wet slate. The silver-green pearl eyes of Thunderbird glistened from an ancestral cone hat.

With reluctant pride, the boy's gaze followed the splendid figure of his clansman. Then he noticed a stranger coming. Walking straight toward Du'as, selecting him from all others, was a youth whose goatskin robe was marked by red stains of ochre.

"Come with me, Du'as," the stranger invited, leading his guest to the rear of the feasthouse. "Sit here with me," he said, indicating a seat that was lost in the deepest shadow.

Dropping down on a cedar mat, Du'as found himself almost behind a projecting totem on a housepost. "This is a poor place to see from," he thought." He was annoyed and puzzled. Why was he hidden here? And what was it that had been missing when the host chiefs had danced their welcome? He frowned. Then, suddenly, he stiffened. "How did he know my name?" he asked himself. Forebodings flooded through the boy again. An appalling thought came to him. The eagle down! The sacred pledge of peace! That had been missing from the Goat chiefs' welcome. He stole an anxious glance at his companion.

Around them the wild drums throbbed faster and faster in the flickering firelight. Above the beat, a chant

rose from the Goat tribe. Dancers circled the flames, wearing grotesque Goat dance masks and casting fantastic shadows.

"Their sacred tribal dance," Du'as noted with quickening interest.

It was an agile leaping dance. At first the performers seemed to exult, like goats free on a mountain. Then, gradually, they began to creep, wary as beasts escaping from cruel hunters.

Faces grew tense around the watching circle.

Du'as was suddenly afraid. There was something

grim about this dancing. There was something ghostly about the Goat-head dance masks. It made him shrink inside; it made his flesh crawl.

Around him the drums throbbed faster and louder, faster and louder. The chant rose higher and higher until it climaxed in a yell—a yell flung out in triumph:

"Behold our prince!"

Another dancer leapt into the circle. Bigger than all the others, he wore a special dance mask. It was a carved goat head, but with a single horn, placed in the center.

"Behold our prince!" Again the yell of triumph.

The prince began to dance; and where he danced, the ground began to rise.

"Some trick," gasped Du'as, but his heart was pounding.

The ground rose up. And up and up. It became a rocky mass, a miniature Stek-yaw-den, with a goat on top of it. For, somehow, the dancing prince had become a living goat. He had turned into a great white buck with one horn on his forehead. He stood defiantly, proud as a Thunderbird and as white as a moonlit birch tree.

Du'as blinked. Perhaps it was some trick. He blinked, and looked again. The one horned goat still stood atop the small Stek-yaw-den.

"The-Great-One-of-the-Hills!" the chant proclaimed him. "When he strikes with his hooves, rocks split asunder! Rocks split like clay baked in the summer sunshine!"

Wide eyed and trembling, the Temlahams sat, waiting.

Caught in a spell, Du'as, like the rest, could move no muscle. In a strange trance, he watched The-Great-One-of-the-Hills trip down the slope, then strike with his hooves against the small magic mountain.

He felt the hard earth quake; he heard it rumble deep in the rocks beneath him; he saw the feasthouse collapse, with its giant timbers. People and poles and flames moved out before him. They dropped in a hideous rockslide. Screams tore the air. Boulders tumbled and crashed and bounced off, thundering down toward the river valley.

Motionless above it all, Du'as trembled, waiting. At last, when he could move, he grabbed for the housepost; but his fingers found sharp spruce needles. Somehow, the housepost had become a spruce tree, a small blue spruce on the edge of a fearful abyss. Scarcely daring to breathe, Du'as turned toward his companion and found a goat whose skin showed stains of red ochre. This was the little kid, he knew, now grown into a young goat. The stains were Grandfather's ointment.

Du'as swallowed, then glanced about in mounting wonder. On every side his recent hosts, now goats as well, were leaping out of danger.

As in the ancient days, the goats had taken human form to avenge the wrongs against them.

"You saved my life," the young goat said, retaining his human voice a little longer. "So I saved yours, to pay the debt I owe you. But listen to me, my brother. Know that the Sky Chief's laws of life go on forever. So does the Sky Chief's power to help his lesser creatures. This you must tell the people."

"But . . . how can . . . ?" Du'as glanced below at the crashing boulders. He dared not move an inch for fear of falling. How could he tell the people? How could he ever reach the river valley?

As though hearing these human thoughts, the young goat answered Du'as. "Put on this goatskin robe," he said. "Put on the sacred headdress." With his black horns, he lifted a goatskin mantle and dropped it over the boy's shoulders. Then he picked up a crestal crown. It was carved with The-One-Horned-Mountain-Goat totem and ringed by sea-lion bristles.

As the sacred regalia dropped on his head and shoulders, Du'as felt more confident. He felt more agile. He moved from the tree to straighten them on his person.

"These are yours now," the goat went on, "as are the Mountain Goat songs and dances. Go to your valley and show these things to remind the people forever that the Sky Chief's laws of life are everlasting."

Wearing his Goat regalia, Du'as found himself nimble and sure among the tumbling boulders. His agile leaps soon took him down the mountain, home to a mourning village. There, the people who had stayed at home had blackened their faces with ash and put on their sorrow-tatters. Wailing ancient clan dirges, they filled the air with sadness.

When they saw Du'as returning home from Stek-yaw-den, they all cried for joy. The old carver and Katla paddled across to meet him.

"Du'as, Du'as, Du'as!" sobbed Katla, flinging her arms around her beloved brother.

The carver greeted his grandson with equal joy. Then he examined the new headdress. A great new totem, he knew, had come to Temlaham, sent by the goats who had punished a cruel people. It would take its place among the clan's honored emblems. Its story would live forever in the Temlaham tribe's traditions. Its dances would shake the feastlodges of descendents for untold ages.

The One-Horned Mountain Goat was Du'as's coat-of-arms all through his life. When he died, his heirs, his sister's sons, inherited the crest with its songs and dances. Thus, down through the years, the totem lived on with its story, reminding the people to have respect for every living creature.

If you see the One-Horned Mountain Goat carved on a totem pole, you will know that totem pole was raised in honor of some heir (inheriting through the long line of Du'as's sister's sons and their sisters' sons and their sisters' sons . . .). You will know, too, that when it was raised at a great potlatch gathering, somebody told this story.

Since Stek-yaw-den means Painted Goat, there are those who think the mountain did not receive that name until after the mountain goats' feast. There are more, however, along the Ksan River (the Skeena River), who have never even heard the name Stek-yaw-den.

"Rocher de Boule," they call the ancient mountain.

Two

AMONG the North Pacific tribes, every true name was the cherished possession of the clan or family. It could not be given until it had been vacated by its previous owner. Even when it had become available, it could not be given lightly or without due ceremony. It had to be merited.

"The Boy and the Sea Monsters" tells a legend of a boy who earned his name in a most difficult way. The story also indicates the special dangers the sea held for primitive man. The sea can inspire terror even today, but to primitive Indians it was a much more mysterious and terrifying region. There were dread storm spirits who, if angered, might stir up fearful tempests. There were sea monsters lurking in every shadow. Dangers like these could not be met with ordinary human sea skill and courage.

To combat these terrors, the Indian might scatter white eagle down, the sacred pledge of peace, respectfully on the waters. He might offer his food and treasures, flinging them humbly into the smoking sea swells. He might even dare to hope for supernatural help, the kind of help that he had heard of in stories about mythical ancestors.

The story of Ice Ribs is one such legend. The hero appears first as a timid boy, and Ice Ribs is merely a nickname, given in scorn until he is worthy of a true name—the name he earns.

The Boy and the Sea Monsters

LONG, LONG AGO, near the beginning of all things, water covered the world. And when the waters receded, they left a swampland, steaming, dank, and gloomy. In the swamp great monsters moved in gigantic armored bodies, terrifying the few people who already walked the earth. As these hid fearfully, they wailed aloud for spirit help.

High, high above them, Supernatural Raven heard the wails. Moved with great pity, he called forth the Thunderbird Tribe from their homes in sky and mountain. The birds thundered down, flashing death at the monsters. Few of the giants escaped, but those who did fled into the sea. There, they lived on in the waters.

Many, many years later two of these great monsters, still wandering the oceans, came to rest near a Haida village. Kagwaii and Kostan, they were, two great primeval monsters. Jawless Kagwaii was a five finned whale who churned through the sea with his giant mouth wide open. Kostan was a crab monster who crushed all that came into his path.

It was Kostan who menaced the Haida people most severely. For the cedar lodges of the village edged a small crescent of beach almost encircled by steep timbered mountains. It was a sheltered cove, with towering rock cliffs at either side of the single channel that led to it. The tide flowed in and ebbed away through this one channel, and through it alone could the sea-roving Haidas seek open water and food. It was in this pass that the great monster Kostan lurked.

Again and again, daring sea-hunters shot out from the village in search of seal, and halibut at their ancestral hunting and fishing stations far from the tribal village. Always, however, two giant pinchers rose up from the water; and monstrous crab arms crushed the dugout canoes as men might crush mere kelp bulbs.

"We will perish," the old women wailed, hugging themselves in their brown cedar garments and rocking themselves on the ground by their painted housefronts. "Can no one slay the dread crab monster, Kostan?"

Many tried, but none succeeded. Many hoped to, but no one could think of a way.

Among those who dared to hope, was a boy called Ice Ribs. Of all who hoped, however, he seemed the least likely to succeed. For although he was the nephew and heir of a great sea hunter, he was fragile and scorned by others. Still he dared to hope. Perhaps he would be the one to think of a brilliant plan to slay the monster. Perhaps he would save the village and shame the boys who had teased and scorned him.

The favorite sport of all the boys was to climb among the rocky ledges of the great cliffs around the village. Here Ice Ribs showed his fear and his timid nature most clearly. He clung to the rocks and moved with great care. Still, he did not stay at home. He went, day after day with the other boys.

"Be careful," the boys scoffed one day when he timidly clambered along a high rocky ledge. "Be careful, Ice Ribs; if you fall you may shatter."

"I may shatter your nose," Ice Ribs thought; but he did not dare to say it.

He clung to the rock, by turns cold with fear and hot with anger. Inching sideways and down along a slanting ledge, he wished he were a goat. "I'd show them how to climb," he muttered to himself. "I'd leap behind each one of them, and send them all flying down into the Devilfish den!" But he was not a goat, and his bravery was all in thought and not in action.

"I'll show those boys some day," he burst out to his faithful slave boy, when at last he stood safe on a broad rock much closer to the water. He took a rebellious breath, swelling his slender chest until his ribs strained

at the skin around them. Then his breath went slowly out. His shoulders sagged. And he screwed at his hair topknot with anxious fingers. "I'll show them," he said again, but not so fiercely.

The slave boy pursed his lips and gazed at Ice Ribs sadly. He was fond of his high born master and distressed by his angry bluster. Slowly his cropped head moved from side to side, and his hands beat a tattoo on his bare brown stomach. "Little-Drum-Belly" everyone called him, smiling.

"I'll show them," Ice Ribs declared once more. His dark eyes sought the sea with safe-on-shore dreams of valiant adventure. Then he stole a sideways glance at his slave boy's face, and encouraged by the sympathy he saw there, he confessed his dream.

"Some day . . . some day," he blurted out, "some day I'm going to slay Kostan . . . and . . . Kagwaii, too," he added, flushing.

Drum-Belly's eyes went wide with consternation.

"I could do it," Ice Ribs announced. "I have figured out a plan to kill that monster. If I were Chief, Drum-Belly, I'd get the people to make mountains of sea-lion rawhide and cut it into line as thick and tough as the line whale hunters run out. I'd have them tie it into a giant fish net, a net big enough to stretch like a roof across that narrow part of the canoe pass. Then, I'd have them tie boulders, like anchor stones, to every corner. We'd anchor the corners on the cliffs above the pass. Beside each boulder we'd have strong prying sticks, with men standing by to use them at my signal.

We would watch and wait, and then, when Kostan was right below the gigantic suspended fish net, I'd blast the signal on my cedar whistle. At once men would pry the boulders off the cliffs; the net would drop right over the monster Kostan; he'd be trapped on the bottom like a helpless salmon; and he'd die of starvation while . . . while we hurled rocks at him."

The boy's eyes sparkled like sunlit waves as he revealed his great plan. "It would work," he confided to his startled slave boy.

Little-Drum-Belly stared at his master, his mouth wide open and his fingers drumming. Then, suddenly, he grabbed Ice Rib's fingers. "Come! Tell the Chief!" he cried in wild excitement.

Ice Ribs flushed with pleasure at his slave's admiration. Perhaps he would earn the respect of others, also. Heart beating fast with hope, he let Drum-Belly urge him along toward the Eagle Chief's house.

There the Chief, in turn, let his startled mouth fall open. He stared at Ice Ribs for one long unblinking minute. Then quietly he asked the boy, "Where would you get all the sea lions for mountains of rawhide, Ice Ribs?"

Ice Ribs swallowed hard. The shine went from his eyes. His face flamed with humiliation. Yes, where had he thought he could get so much new rawhide? He cringed inwardly and wished the floor would open. How stupid he must seem!

Filled with blinding shame, he spun around and raced off to hide himself.

How stupid he had been, he kept on thinking. Oh, why had he ever mentioned his wild notion? Now everyone would know him stupid as well as cowardly. Before, they had dubbed him "Ice Ribs." Now, what more might they call him, nudging and laughing, and joking with one another? "The-One-Who-Kills-Sea-Monsters," perhaps.

"I wish I were a clam," he groaned, "buried deep in the sand and shut up in a clamshell." He threw himself down on some moss alone. But he was not alone for long. Soon a faithful shadow fell across him.

"It . . . was . . . a good plan," panted Little-Drum-Belly staunchly.

"A good plan to laugh at," stormed Ice Ribs.

"You'll think up another one," the slave boy said, soothing him; and he was right.

Next day Ice Ribs disclosed a second plan. "We could take canoes," he said. "We could lash them together, and then lash drifted logs to encircle them like a fortress, and spike the drift logs with a forest of spears and sharp snags. Then, when Kostan began to crush it—as he always does—he'd impale himself on a giant porcupine-thing. That way, we would use his own strength to pierce his soft under-belly."

The boy's eyes shone with triumph, then dulled with the thought that this, too, might be stupid.

As before, Little-Drum-Belly was flatteringly astounded. His mouth dropped open. His fingers drummed with excitement. "Tell the Chief," he urged once more. But coax as he might, this time he failed to budge his master.

"I'm not going to be laughed at," Ice Ribs protested.

Yet still he dreamed of ways to save the village. Next day, another plan was ready.

It was at low tide that he revealed it. The two boys were sunning themselves on a broad rock shelf that had emerged, wet, from the sea when the tide had ebbed. Above their heads, white sea gulls rode air currents. A brown osprey eyed them from a silvered tree snag. And high over all, an enormous eagle circled.

"This plan is different," Ice Ribs explained, half frowning. "We'd entangle the monster first, not kill him outright." Hesitation betrayed some lingering doubt of this plan. "First we'd . . . we'd lash drift logs together. Then . . . then we'd encircle the logs with a gigantic tangle. We'd make that of fish net, rawhide, and kelp tubes—those big kelp tubes that are as long as a house and as thick as your arm, Drum-Belly. Then . . . then we'd tie on whaling floats to keep it buoyant. We could use those sea-lion air sacs that can keep a harpooned whale from sounding. Then . . . then . . . when it was big and strong enough, canoes would push it while the tide was ebbing. The tide race would take it rushing through the channel. Kostan's arms would rise and get caught in the tangle. He'd be held to the surface by the bobbing air sacs. He'd be swept out of the channel by the tidal current . . . and . . . and . . . and he'd get caught up on the reef outside or . . . or . . . or he'd get lost at sea or something." His eyes lost their shine before he had finished speaking.

"It . . . might work," Little-Drum-Belly agreed, though his voice lacked much conviction.

Lost in their own concerns, neither noticed a fleeting darkness. Neither boy looked up as a huge wingspread cut off the sun and moved like a cloud shadow over the rocks around them.

Yet, without realizing why, Ice Ribs thought of the Thunderbirds and of how the monsters had first been killed. "We need supernatural help," he told Drum-Belly. "With spirit aid, we could get Kostan up where a Thunderbird could kill him."

This new idea sparked his imagination. Supernatural help, he knew, was not uncommon. Many people gained power that was far beyond their own. Usually it came to them when they had gone to seek it, alone, high in the hills. It came to them while they were fasting there, awaiting their spirit vision.

"Perhaps I . . ." Bright with new hope, Ice Ribs lifted his eyes toward the mountains and then widened them in dismay. There the rain forest grew, dark green and dank and gloomy. There every living sound was muffled by thick wet mosses. Slinking wolves glided among the trees, he knew, and bears. Gray slimy slugs trailed everywhere. He shuddered to think of the evil swamps and eerie howls and ghostly visitations.

Guiltily his gaze returned to the lightness of the sun and the sea gulls. He swallowed and admitted it took more courage than he possessed to win great spirit power. The tribe would starve to death; Ice Ribs could never save it.

He turned to speak to Drum-Belly. But the slave boy was gone. Had he run to the village to tell the Eagle Chief about the two new stupid plans? Ice Ribs squirmed at the prospect of more taunts and nudgings.

He wished he was brave enough to leap into the sea and swim away forever; but since he lacked that courage, he hoped the tide would take him. He stretched out in the sun with glum abandon while the world around him grew warm and hushed and drowsy. A soothing breeze stirred lazily through the pine trees. The sea flowed in, in slow undulations, lulling even the gulls with its gentle rolling motion.

Then the eagle came.

The tide was licking up toward his shelf when Ice Ribs sensed his bright world darken. Aware this time, he sprang up to see what caused it.

A blackness seemed to blot the sun. Then Ice Ribs saw the bird, an enormous hovering eagle. Its talons were extended, clutching something. It was something that moved and twisted, that glinted with living copper.

Then in one swift slanting plunge, the eagle rushed down toward Ice Ribs's rock shelf.

Ice Ribs dived, too, straight down into some crackling seaweed. He hid his face and waited, almost breathless. He heard a whirrr, a thud, then a thunder of rising wing beats. The eagle had come and gone, leaving something alive behind it.

It was a fish, a gigantic flopping gray fish.

"A halibut," gasped Ice Ribs, daring to go closer. "But what a size!" One swipe of that great tail would send him sprawling. He backed away to a more respectful distance.

The fish was strangely colored. A stripe of copper scales banded the body like a glistening necklace, enlivening the gray scales around it. Still, it was a fish.

"A meal for Eagle House," Ice Ribs cried. "Club it!" he ordered, forgetting his slave boy's absence. Then his heart seemed to stop as the giant fish flopped over.

It slid toward the water.

"We'll lose the fish! We'll lose the fish!" he shouted.

He glanced toward the village with impatience. It would be useless to call for help. The wind was against him. Oh, why had Drum-Belly gone off when he was needed?

The fish flopped once again and slipped toward the sea. The boy glanced all about in desperation. There was no help for it; he must kill the fish himself, or he would lose it. He grabbed his club. With hammering heart, he darted in to use it. Then, closing his eyes, he whacked.

Amazingly, at his first blow the huge fish lay still and lifeless.

"I've . . . killed it," he breathed. But even as he exulted, he noticed that the tide had reached his rock shelf. The sea would claim his fish before he could begin to move it.

"I'll have to run for help," Ice Ribs decided. Yet, somehow, he could not move. He tried to shout, but he could not make one sound come out. A feeling of terror gripped him. He was completely helpless; the tide might take him with the fish that he had slaughtered. His will no longer ruled his body; some greater will had captured it. He was stunned by its tremendous power.

Caught in its dread compulsion, he reached for his mussel shell knife. Then, through no will of his own and with uncanny skill, he began to skin the great fish. Surprisingly, its skin slipped off as easily as skin slips off a boiled fish; yet this skin was strong and pliant. Its copper scales shone with a special brilliance.

Copper! Something tugged at Ice Ribs's thoughts as he worked with his fingers. Copper? Copper? His mind searched through old stories until they reached Copper Woman. She had used the copper sign on all her magic. Had the eagle been Copper Woman disguised as a bird to bring this great fish to him? But why to him? Surely she would choose a brave boy for her unknown purpose! Yet a mighty power now occupied his body. It was using his hands to wield a mussel shell knife.

When the skin had been cut free, it was like a glistening garment. Still not willing what he did, Ice Ribs wrapped it around his body. Then he lay down on the rock in the rising water, and he heard his own voice express an astounding desire:

"I wish I were a halibut."

At once he was a fish. He was slithering along wet seaweed toward the rock's edge. Helpless to stop himself, he slid down into the deep cold water, down down toward the Devilfish den. An instant of panic seized him. Then a wild new craving caught his strange new body. It was a craving for deeper water. He kicked, and his bulk shot forward. His feet were now tailfins, but he could use them. He could use them at his will! He could scull with them, and his body, now big and strange and smooth, slipped through the water with the speed of a silver salmon.

He was sure now of what had happened. Forced

by another's will, he had donned a supernatural garment. With the garment had come its special guise
and spirit power, but not a will to use them. His will
was his own again to guide his actions. He was still
Ice Ribs, the boy with dreams of valor; but now he was
disguised as a fish and made mighty with spirit power.
He thrilled with the wonder of it.

To test his new found power, he dodged in and out
through a forest of anchored kelp tubes. He flicked
his fins at a rabble of gaping bullheads. He darted
daringly close to the murk of the Devilfish den. Then,
convinced of his power, he made straight for the channel where Kostan was lurking. At last Ice Ribs would
save the village. Exhileration filled him.

But how big the crab monster looked when he
swam near it! It appeared as huge as a feasthouse and
as fierce as a whole dread tribe of Devilfishes. His
halibut form seemed, suddenly, rather puny.

He twisted about and dashed toward the shelter
of the cove and village. But scorning himself, he turned
again toward the channel. With pounding heart and
stealthy care, he ventured along the rock wall. He
darted, and dodged, and escaped from the deadly
pinchers. Then with mighty swipes of his great tail,
he made fast for the open water. He skirted the reef
that lay close to the channel entrance.

Soon he found himself in the broad sea swells outside the channel, near a tribe of playful porpoises. He
relaxed in the lovely water; let it lap around him. The
cool green smoothness flowed caressingly past his

body. The sound of the sea was soothing. Perhaps, he thought, he would laze along forever, forgetting he was human.

Then he felt a change. The porpoises darted off, streaking outward in all directions. He sensed a frightful churning close behind him. With a sinking heart, he guessed what it was. It was dread Kagwaii coming. It was the primeval whale who moved through the sea with his monstrous mouth wide open.

Ice Ribs sculled wildly, flailing his mighty tail fins; yet the monster gained on him with every moment. He spurted, twisted, dived; but the giant beast came closer, faster and faster through the wake behind him. Then a blackness engulfed him, and he knew that he had been swallowed. He, Ice Ribs in fish disguise, was trapped in a monster's belly. He was stunned by the horror of it.

He longed for a spear or harpoon, though as a fish he could never use one. He yearned for even his trusty fish knife. "How I wish I were a human!" he thought.

Instantly, as he made the wish, he felt a swift conversion. A startling change transformed him. He had arms and legs again, and a mussel shell knife and fingers. He was Ice Ribs once more—Ice Ribs trapped in a monster's belly! He grabbed for his knife. Then, holding his breath, he slashed with desperate courage at the monster's vitals all around him.

Finally, wishing himself a fish once more, he weathered the storm of Kagwaii's death convulsions. Awaiting his chance, he slipped out of the fearful cavern.

He felt a fierce triumph race through his fish body. He had killed a dread sea monster, and he had done it as Ice Ribs, the frightened human. That knowledge gave him boundless reassurance. It gave him self respect. He, Ice Ribs, had killed Kagwaii as he had said he would; and somehow, he knew, he would slay the monster Kostan.

"I'll go back to the channel now," he thought, but he could not flick the right fins. He tried again, and again, but he could not do it. He was caught in a spell once more, in the power of the circling eagle. So, unable to do otherwise, he stayed with the drifting carcass until it was washed ashore on a lonely island.

There, a boy once more, Ice Ribs worked with skill that was not his own to skin the body. When he laid bare a bit of rib, it seemed to be not bone, but an arched shaft of glittering white quartz. "Old Stone Ribs," he gloated, using his tribe's translation of the name, Kagwaii. "Ice Ribs has killed old Stone Ribs." The thought delighted him. How he wished he could tell Drum-Belly!

When he had finished the skinning, he fastened the precious halibut garment around his slender waist. Then, caught in the strange compulsion still, he dragged Kagwaii's skin into deep water and swam right into it, letting it float about him.

"I wish I were Stone Ribs," his voice said.

Instantly, startlingly, he was Stone Ribs!

Disguised now as a monster whale, Ice Ribs threshed through the ocean with his mouth wide open. He swam. He sounded. He spouted high. "But always at my will!" he rejoiced. As once before, a supernatural garment had brought him its guise and power, but not its will. That was his own again. He could choose what he would do with this great body.

That thought came to him like a clap of thunder.

He could choose what he would do with this great body. He could swim away forever, leaving a scornful tribe to face starvation. Or he could do what he had dreamed he would. He could kill Kostan and save his native village.

"So . . . now for Kostan!" he thought, heading straight for the channel where the crab was lurking.

As he neared the passage, though, he felt misgivings. The crab was huge and very strongly armored. It had many arms and legs. It had vicious snapping pinchers. Otherwise, he decided, their two strengths were roughly equal.

"But I have a human's thinking," he told himself to bolster his sinking courage. "Am I not Ice Ribs who makes brilliant plans to outwit an adversary?"

Before he could plan one move, however, the monster crab was on him. Arms clamped like a trap around him. Jagged pinchers gouged his flesh. Clawing legs tore at his body.

"A plan!" he begged himself as he writhed and turned to free his wounded body. "I must have a plan to kill old Kostan." But his mind refused to function. The fear of death froze his imagination.

"Perhaps . . ." An anguished thought came. Perhaps this was a hideous joke of Copper Woman's—to give him the power he had craved and then show him that he could not use it. Well, he would not give up so easily.

For hours the two monsters fought. They wallowed together in murky depths, lashing fiercely at one another. They churned the sea into foam. Again and again, Ice Ribs tried to crush the crab against the rock wall but was bruised himself against it. He tried to wrench a crab arm off, but was ripped instead by pinchers. He tried to stun the crab with his great tail fin, but the channel was too confining.

"A plan!" he implored himself. He groped wildly to find a good one, but none came to his mind even now when his need was desperate. He was going to lose this fight and die.

He sensed the tidal current flowing past him. The tide was ebbing. Soon it would be out. But there was hope in that! At low tide a submerged reef would surface outside the cove, quite near the channel entrance. If he could move the battle to it!

At last he had a plan. It was a desperate plan to use the creature's strength against itself. It would kill itself; and him, perhaps. But using his human wit, there was still one chance to conquer.

In order to help himself and give him courage, he thought of the crab as "it," not "he." His alone was the human will.

Ice Ribs bent his efforts now to move the struggle outward, out with the tide, toward that ridge of granite. He twisted and writhed with pain, but his tail fins kept on sculling.

At last the reef lay just ahead. It was a submerged ridge of mountain peaks lying very near the surface. Above it a black cloud hovered.

Saving his strength, he let the tide race take him. He let Kostan straddle his giant side without resisting.

Once astride his bulk, the crab clamped its death grip on him, while Ice Ribs feebly flicked his fins to steer the two giant bodies. When he touched the reef, he made two last wild tail sweeps, propelling his form along the biting granite. The hard peaks gouged his

flesh. They ripped his fins, but they held him there as his dreadful plan demanded.

Almost dead from these final wounds, he gathered his forces for one last mighty effort. In one grim burst of strength, he strained outward with his body. He strained upward and out, against the encircling crab arms.

In swift response, the creature tightened its grip with its own last pound of pressure.

Instantly, at tension's height, Ice Ribs wished himself a halibut and was squirted out, in a mighty WHOOSH, from the whale's collapsing body.

The monster crab, caught at its greatest stress, crashed down on the jagged peaks and cracked its belly. Then it sprawled inert, impaled on rock and tangled in the tattered whale skin.

Ice Ribs, now halibut, surfaced to look and saw also that a storm was building. Perhaps it was the Thunderbirds, come to kill as he, Ice Ribs had once predicted. With awe, he darted off toward the sheltered cove and village.

Once through the channel, he swam across the cove toward the rock shelf. There he regained his human form to fall, prostrate, in complete exhaustion. He felt battered and bruised in mind as well as body, but a triumph filled his soul. He had done the deed that he had dreamed of.

His precious fish skin slipped from his fingers as a quick storm broke around him. Thunder cracked about his unconscious head; lightning flashed on his bleeding body, but Ice Ribs lay still as death.

Later, when the storm had passed, he was roused by an eagle's plunging. He heard a whirrr, a cry, then a thunder of wing beats; and he raised his head in time to catch a fleeting glint of copper. The eagle had come and gone, and with it had taken its glistening garment.

"Gone," groaned Ice Ribs, his triumph collapsing like the skin of old dead Kagwaii. With the supernatural garment had gone its spirit power and the courage it had given him. With the garment had gone the thrilling joy that had raced through his body. His head sagged down, his shoulders slumped, and he sighed with a hopeless sadness. He was only Ice Ribs once more, without courage or strength or daring.

Then he saw his slave boy leaping the rocks toward him.

"There's been a monsters' battle," Drum-Belly yelled. "Kostan is dead. The Thunderbirds have killed him."

"I know," Ice Ribs replied. "I planned his slaughter."

Little-Drum-Belly stared hard at his battered master, his mouth wide open and his fingers drumming.

"I'll tell you all about it," Ice Ribs offered. And he told his slave the whole fantastic story.

"But . . . but . . . but . . . but . . ." Drum-Belly spluttered at him.

"It happened," Ice Ribs insisted, shrilly.

"Then . . . then . . . then . . . tell the Chief,"

the astounded slave boy urged him.

"I'm not going to be laughed at," Ice Ribs protested, flushing.

"Then I will tell him," Drum-Belly said, and was off like a startled duckling.

Ice Ribs lay down again, feeling as tattered and torn as the skin of old dead Kagwaii. "The-Boy-Who-Killed-Sea-Monsters," they would dub him, laughing and nudging and joking with one another. Not one of them would believe he had had a great adventure. They would say his wounds came from tumbling off rock ledges.

The tide was almost in when his slave boy came back.

"You're to come to the Chief," he ordered.

Ice Ribs just shrugged. Accepting his dismal fate, he stumbled along in silence.

Walking saggingly in behind his slave, Ice Ribs found the feasthouse crowded. People were gathered as if they were awaiting an Eagle potlatch. Head men wore their regalia. Drum boxes throbbed. Red flames were leaping high toward the smokehole while masked dancers circled, making fantastic shadows. And a hubbub of happy voices ringed the lodge fire.

"Of course," he realized, "celebrating the tribe's delivery." Perhaps, after all, he might slip unnoticed to some shadowed corner.

But Little-Drum-Belly led him straight to the place of honor. Only when he had placed his master before the Eagle Chief, did he slide away and leave him.

Ice Ribs stood there before his Chief, his forlorn features downcast. He expected a stern reproof for what others would think was boastful chatter.

"You are strong and brave, Ice Ribs."

Astounded, the boy glanced up. He could not have heard aright. In amazement, his mouth dropped open.

"You are strong and brave, Ice Ribs."

The Chief had said those words. Twice he had said them. Convinced of this, Ice Ribs shook his head in a bitter but firm denial.

"The bravery and strength were not my own," he answered. "They were spirit power. They have gone with the skin that brought them." He knew himself for what he was, a miserable timid creature. Without spirit help, he was fearful of his own shadow. "The courage I had is gone," he said. "It was lost with the skin that brought it."

"Perhaps it can be regained," the Chief said kindly.

Ice Ribs felt strong hands laid then upon his shoulders. "Your name will be Stone Ribs," a voice informed him.

For a moment the boy just stood there, stunned and silent. Then his voice awoke. "Stone Ribs? Stone Ribs!" It was a name vacated by the biggest whale that had ever come into their waters. What power must be in it! "Stone Ribs!" he cried again, in glad excitement.

The clan had adopted a great new name and made him its first human wearer. The boy straightened his slender height to bear so great an honor. A strong name, he knew, was like a supernatural garment. It brought you its spirit power, though not the will to use it. That you must bring yourself, and that he could bring. He had proved that to himself in his encounter. He could meet the challenge of it.

A thought came to him then. The tribe had entrusted him with a great new name, so they must believe his story. He glanced about the lodge with wistful eagerness. Meeting smiling eyes, he sensed a different feeling. He knew what they believed, those watching people. They thought he had had a vision, alone on a sunwarmed rock shelf. They thought that only his spirit had ventured out through the waters.

Strangely, somehow, that did not seem to matter. He knew what he knew, himself. That was what counted. New self respect was wrapped about him like a protecting fur robe.

Next day he played again on the rocky ledges.

"Be careful, Stone Ribs," a voice called out. "If you fall, you may shatter."

"I may shatter the rocks," he gayly yelled in answer. And he found himself laughing with all the boys around him. At last, the boys' barbs could not prick him to foolish anger. He was armored with confidence. He was Stone Ribs, a proven person.

A few weeks later, excitement stirred the village. Fish nets had caught small crabs, tiny living replicas of the once-dreaded Kostan. And the crabs were good to eat, the tribe discovered.

"This is the work of Raven," people whispered.

"Raven the Trickster, has played a prank on Kostan. He has transformed the monster's shattered bits into seafood to feed the village. Instead of starving us, the monster feeds us." They laughed delightedly at such a notion.

"Raven has played a prank on us, as well," agreed Stone Ribs, wryly amused by a small attacking creature. He pulled one foot out of the water, chuckling. Two sharp pinchers were clinging to it.

Little-Drum-Belly stared in pleased surprise at this new joking master. Then he darted back in haste to avoid his own small sea monster.

Three

EVEN TODAY, Indians of the North Pacific coast turn their faces to the sea and their backs to the mountains, for the wilderness on land is not inviting.

There the rain forest broods. Where the westerly winds strike the high coastal range after crossing the Pacific Ocean, the resulting rainfall and the mild climate produce heavy stands of tall dark timber. Dense undergrowth makes the forest an almost impenetrable jungle. Thick mosses muffle swamps and rocks and deadfalls. Even the birds shun the rain forest's silence. Only wolves and other fearsome things creep through its frightening shadows.

In the long ago days, ignorance and imagination added even more terrors. Every Indian tribe knew of ogres and witches who lived deep in the forest. And although she was called different names by the various tribes, one of these fierce creatures was always a giantess who lurked about to catch children, the Wild Woman of the Woods. Tezlemokg (Tez-le-mok-guh) she was called by the Tsimshians of this legend.

But evil creatures were not the only supernatural beings Indians knew. Lacking science, the aboriginies found fanciful reasons for the mysteries of nature. The sky was the blue floor of a land up above them. In this Above Land, or Sky Land, lived other supernatural creatures. These were not unfriendly, though inclined to be gay and full of tricks. Such a being is the spirit boy who comes into this story.

His means of coming to earth, and of returning to the sky, are popular traditions in folk tales from the north coast. What he does to the ogress delighted Indians, who possessed a lively sense of humor.

The Wild Woman of the Woods

ONCE UPON A TIME there was a little girl whose name
was Bidal. She could never understand why people considered her a nuisance, even when she lingered far
behind or was never ready when others were. She was
only looking for pretty things, so why should they be
impatient?

When she would linger along a forest trail, searching for tiny pink bells among the lacy mosses, some
one was sure to shout, "Come on, Bidal! Don't
dawdle!" Or when she would lag behind on the beach
to hunt for seashells, some one would surely call out,

"Do hurry up, Bidal! Why must you be such a nuisance?"

Bidal was a Raven Crest child in a Tsimshian tribe of Indians. The cedar houses of her village fronted along a beach, pushed almost into the sea by the dark-timbered mountains that crowded close behind them. When the tide was in, the carved portal pole of her house nearly waded in the water.

Living in the same big Raven families' house was an older girl, Gundax. Her mat lay next to Bidal's on the long sleeping platform. And Gundax was especially impatient with Bidal.

Sometimes when the small girl was not sleepy, she would want to talk about the starry sparks that leapt up toward the smokehole. But Gundax would scold and say, "Don't be a nuisance, Bidal!" If she were very cross, she would snap, "Oh hush, you stupid child, or Tezlemokg will hear you!"

Tezlemokg was the Wild Woman of the Woods. She was the giantess who lived in the deep, dark forest. She captured unwary children.

"Hush!" Gundax would fiercely whisper. "Sh, sh, Bidal! I think I hear her coming."

The little girl would shiver down into her rabbit-skins. She would cover up her ears and try not to hear a dreadful "Ooo-ooo-eee-ooo!" shrilling above the wind that tossed the pines and creaked the cedars. She would squeeze her eyelids shut and try not to peek at a flickering house post that was carved like the lurking ogress. Supporting a great roof beam, it was a towering wooden image with staring holes for eyes, and a rounded calling mouth, and ears spread wide to catch the slightest murmur.

"Now hush!" Gundax would warn, "Or Tezlemokg will catch you!"

"Would . . . would she put me into her basket?" Bidal would dare to whisper. "And . . . and shut my eyes with pitch? Would she take me through the forest and . . . and . . . eat me up? Would . . . would she?"

"Of course she would. So shush!" Gundax would hiss. Sometimes, when she had terrified Bidal, she would sneak away and leave her. The little girl would sob and have a nightmare; but Gundax was unconcerned.

And so it went until one lovely day when the sun shone brightly on the deep cold sea and on the little village. It was morning and the tide was going out, leaving wet seaweed steaming and crackling along the big gray rocks that edged the dark rain forest. Small rocky tidal pools were alive with tiny darting things, and the sandy beach was spouting with many clams.

Women in loose brown cedar garments were gathering along the beach with digging sticks to get all the clams they could to dry for winter. Tall boys came, too, with digging sticks and baskets to put the clams in.

Little Bidal came, also. Her small seashell basket hung on her bare brown back, held by a forehead tumpline. Delightedly she put it down beside a pool and started to look for limpets.

Because her chosen pool was high on a treacherous rock, her mother tried to move her. "Go with the other children," Sudaol urged her daughter. "Go where Gundax can watch you." She saw that the rock was jagged with barnacles and slippery with wet brown seaweed. "Bidal," she urged again, "why don't you go with Gundax?"

"Because . . ." Bidal looked down and screwed one foot beneath her. "Because I have to gather limpet shells."

"Here, on the rocks? And now, when the clams are spouting?" Sudaol scanned the busy beach. "Not now!" she protested. "Not now when the clams are spouting!"

"But it's best now," Bidal insisted. "And the rocky pools are clearest." Her black eyes searched the lovely pool that lay waiting at her feet. She saw tiny glistening moon shells, and snail shells aswirl with color. "I need more limpet shells," she coaxed. She looked into her basket and ran her hands through hundreds of shells that looked like tiny spruce root cone-hats woven with blues and grays and browns in dainty patterns. "I need to fill my basket up with limpets."

"Well," said her mother, sighing impatiently, "all right, Bidal. But watch that slippery seaweed!" Shrugging off her fears, she left her child and joined the busy diggers.

The little girl squatted happily beside her pool, searching for limpet shells. She found white ones and patterned ones, all shaped like tiny cone-hats. She considered a mussel shell. It was big and sharp edged, but it gleamed with lovely blue mother-of-pearl; so she popped it in with her other shells. And then she found a prize. It was a pale brown limpet shell, circled on top by a white barnacle that had been polished and smoothed by water.

"It looks like a chief's hat, topped by a ring to show he has had a potlatch," she thought in great delight. Wanting to show her mother, she called loudly for Sudaol.

At her cry, her mother leapt toward her, scudding across the beach and over the rocks and seaweed. "You've hurt yourself?" she asked, grasping the small bare shoulders.

"No," Bidal answered, surprised by the anxious question. "But look at this chief's hat limpet!"

"You called me just for that?" Sudaol demanded.

"But . . . don't you like to look at pretty things?"

"Not when I'm busy. Now don't call me again unless you need me!"

"I won't," the small girl promised; but she forgot her promise. Three times again she shrieked and brought her mother running.

"You are a nuisance," Sudaol snapped. "You're wasting my morning, Bidal. Now, do as you're told! Go where Gundax can mind you!"

Bidal picked up her basket very slowly, setting the tumpline square across her forehead. No matter what she did, she was a nuisance. And she was only hunting for pretty things. Blinking back tears, she walked toward the other children, who were playing potlatch at the far end of the beach.

These were the common children of the village; noble folk had slaves to mind their children. Gundax looked after these at times like this, but she was cross and lazy. She slapped and scolded them. She even scowled on this lovely day at a watching raven.

He was a big old raven, wise with his eighty years, and as black as a charred wood cinder. Crafty, like all his tribe, he kept a sharp eye on everybody. Using his voice in clever imitation, he mocked Gundax; and his lively old eyes watched Bidal coming.

Although she was fond of the raven, Bidal answered his perky glance with only a dismal teardrop. She did not feel like talking to him, nor to the children either. Instead she stood, forlorn and glum, watching the game of potlatch.

Pretending that Gundax was a chieftainess, the children were scurrying about to find food for her feast and gifts for her visitors.

"Here are seagull eggs," one child cried out, dumping smooth pebbles out of a large white clamshell.

"Here's seals," another added, contributing brown kelp heads.

"I'm carving spoons for gifts," a girl told Bidal. She was cutting kelp tube with a bit of broken blue mussel shell.

"Spoons?" scoffed Gundax, scowling down at the small girl's efforts. Then she turned her frown on Bidal. "I have to mind you, too?" she asked her crossly.

"No, you don't have to mind me," answered Bidal. "I'll play with my shells myself."

"Shells?" queried Gundax. She dipped rude hands into the seashell basket. "Why, these are limpet shells! They'll do for spruce-root-hats for potlatch giving." She yanked at the pretty basket; she slapped sharply at clinging fingers. "Let go, Bidal!" she ordered.

"No, no, they're mine!" Bidal clutched at her tumpline. She yelled, and kicked with her small hard feet. She jabbed with her elbows wildly.

"You eight armed Devilfish!" Gundax clouted the flailing fury. "Give me those limpets, Bidal!"

"I won't! I won't! They're mine!" Bidal kept kicking fiercely. She was fighting to save her treasures.

"All right for you," snapped Gundax, rubbing one shinbone grimly. "I'll let Tezlemokg fix you, Bidal." She turned brashly toward the nearby trees, circling her hands to make a speaking funnel. "Tezlemokg!" she called out, sending the frightening summons through the forest. "Tezlemokg, come for Bidal!"

Bidal stood, stunned. The other children huddled nearby in silence. All terrified, they watched the dark green trees that loomed so close before them.

"Tezlemokg!" Gundax called out again. Then she gasped in fear to see tall hemlocks parting. "It's . . ." Swallowing the dreadful name, she collapsed in fright, caught by her own brash summons.

It was Tezlemokg.

She stood there, a towering giantess, an ugly ogress with deepset eyes and with ears spread wide to catch the slightest murmur. A basket tumpline lay across her forehead. One hand held a nettle fish net.

"I'll give my shells! I'll give my shells!" Bidal offered in screaming panic.

Struck speechless with horror, every other child seemed rooted there beside her.

"Ooo-ooo-eee-ooo-OOO!"

Tezlemokg gave one screech of triumph, then flung her net. It dropped over the trembling huddle. It pulled the children in as a salmon net pulls salmon. Then, like a salmon catch, it spilled them into her giant basket: Gundax, Bidal, and five other screaming children. Their shrieks for help were lost by the wayward winds, then muffled by trees and mosses.

Bidal could not even scream. The Wild Woman of the Woods had caught her. She had put her into her basket. She was closing her eyes with pitch now. Then she would carry her into the deep dark forest and . . . Her mind did not dare to finish.

Only the old black raven saw them go off. Craftily he followed the giantess to find out where her lodge was. He moved with such stealth that not one of the children heard him as they whimpered and jostled inside of the dreadful basket.

"It's all your fault, Bidal," Gundax scolded the child. She struggled to get on top. "You would be selfish, you, you snivelling nuisance!" Planting her big bare feet on heads and arms and stomachs, she tried to get out; but the net was doubled tight and strong across the basket. It held her inside with her little charges. "But

I'll get out," she told them.

"You'd only lose your way," a boy piped shrilly. "If we could leave a trail . . ."

"A trail? My shells, my shells, my shells!" squeaked little Bidal.

"Give me those shells!" Gundax clutched about to find the seashell basket. When her rough hands had snatched it up, she hung it about her neck; then she grabbed for shells to toss out.

"There's one sharp musselshell," Bidal warned kindly.

"I know. I cut myself," grumped angry Gundax.

"Why . . . why don't you cut the net?" Bidal suggested.

"Why don't I cut your tongue?" asked Gundax, rudely, but she fished out the musselshell and started working.

"Perhaps . . ." Bidal dared to hope, just for a moment, "perhaps . . ." But she was numbed by a mounting terror. The basket was jogging, jogging, jogging, going deeper and deeper into the dark rain forest. The child's mind closed itself against the horror of what was coming. She slumped down in the basket, scarcely conscious of anybody.

When Gundax's hole was big enough, she stood firmly atop the children. With one hand she reached about above her head, grasping wildly for likely branches; with the other hand she tossed out a trail of seashells. She could not see, of course. She was blinded with pitch as were the children who whimpered beneath her, bruised by her callous efforts.

Suddenly she felt a branch and caught it. Grasping it with both big hands, she let it pull her body from the basket. Once free of that, she scrambled blindly along the branch and down the tree trunk. Then, ridding her eyes of pitch enough to see, she peered fearfully around her.

How gloomy it seemed! How muffled with thick wet mosses! How quiet the forest was. It seemed as still as a lonely graveyard. It was eerie and dark and awful.

Then Gundax glimpsed a limpet shell. It lay on dark moss, as pale as a moon in daylight. She lunged for it, and dropped it into the seashell basket. The chink of striking shells broke up the stillness, the awful brooding stillness of the forest.

Her eyes peered through the gloom to find another shell, then another, and then another. Watching for limpet shells, she moved down the mountain slope past mossy rocks and muskeg swamps and Devil's Club; on and on and on through the dreadful silence.

Each time she found a shell, she picked it up and dropped it into the seashell basket, to hear the sound it made.

At long long last, she heard the surf and the screaming sea gulls. Then she glimpsed the lovely sky, and then the cedar houses. She saw people running anxiously toward her.

"Where are the children, Gundax?" they shouted.

"With Tezlemokg," she answered. "I . . . I tried

to save them all, but when I couldn't, I rushed back here for help." It was the first time she had given a thought to even one of her little charges.

"That's Bidal's basket!" Sudaol took it, sobbing, "And all her little shells." She sobbed still harder.

"I made a trail of shells," said Gundax, smugly.

"And picked it up?" a father thundered at her.

"Well, I . . . I . . ." She spluttered in guilt, her mean eyes growing sullen.

"You stupid wretch!" the whole tribe stormed at Gundax.

"We'll find the trail," Sudaol vowed, but men shook their heads in answer. They knew the rain forest. It was spongy with thick damp moss and swampy muskeg. No trail would show.

Nevertheless, they went into its gloom with torches. They searched all night, then searched again in daylight. They searched and searched and searched, but it was useless. The trail was lost in all that springing dampness. So, admitting at last that the children were lost to them, families blackened their faces with ash and filled the air with sadness.

Again and again the old black raven flapped his wings and screeched at them, but they paid no attention to him.

Then something startling happened to Sudaol.

She was sitting grieving beside a tidal pool, with a circle of friends around her. In her lap lay Bidal's basket and a scatter of pretty seashells. As she softly moaned and rocked herself, tears fell into the tiny hat shaped shells.

Suddenly, one of her hovering friends stiffened. "Look, look!" she urged. "Look at that pure white limpet shell! Look at the tears inside it!"

"Why . . . they're thickening," an old woman gasped, awe stricken. "And they're quivering . . . as if with life."

All stared in fright and wonder. The tears in one small shell were thickening; they were quivering as if with life. They were gathering a form and radiance.

As the people watched spellbound, a tiny glistening child took shape, a spirit boy. He sprang from Sudaol's

teardrops. And there before their eyes, he grew until he was a shining youth with skin like pearl and hair as golden as summer sunbeams. His breech-clout and headband were as silver as living salmon. From each ear hung clustering discs of rainbow-pearl abalone. Looking at him was like seeing the sun through opalescent sea mist. And when he spoke, his voice was as bright as morning.

"Why do you weep, Sudaol?"

"Because my child is lost," she whispered, dazzled and fascinated.

The raven cried out shrilly and beat his wings, but still nobody noticed.

"I have come to find Bidal," the youth informed them. "I have come to find the child who may open your eyes to beauty."

"There is no trail," breathed Sudaol.

The raven stretched his wings and scolded at her.

"He says there is a trail," the youth translated.

"You understand the raven?" people asked him, blinking in yet more wonder.

"Do you not understand him? When he speaks so clearly?"

Mollified by these flattering words, the bird strutted to a driftlog. Perching on top of it, he stretched his neck to make triumphant noises. Then, spreading his wings, he flew into the forest.

"We go for the children now." The shining one spoke; then he was gone. It was as if he had never been there.

"Did we just dream him?" the people asked one another; yet they looked with hope up toward the mountain.

Following the raven, the spirit boy fled through the brooding forest. There was scarcely a quivering leaf to mark his passage. As he moved, he only cast a strange green light on things around him. Swiftly he flashed under the evergreens, through the thick underbrush, and over the springing mosses until finally he came to a mountain pool that mirrored a slanting pine tree.

"Thank you, Grandfather Raven," he said.

They had reached the spring where Tezlemokg came for her water. For a moment the youth stood thinking, then he spoke to the murmuring raven.

"She must be tricked, you say? Well, I shall trick her!"

The raven gurgled gayly from the pine tree. Born of a crafty tribe, he delighted to see wit matched with stupid bigness. He stretched his neck, bubbling over with bright suggestions. Then he flew to the ogress's nearby lodge to peek in at the captured children.

He saw them there, hung up in a net to smoke like a catch of salmon. A smudge of rotten hemlock burned beneath them. But they were alive! They whimpered and coughed and cried out. Still, there was no time to lose, he reported when he returned to the slanting pine tree.

"Then we shall lose no time," the youth assured him.

The raven squawked a warning from the pine tree.

Tezlemokg was coming. The mosses vibrated with the shock of her heavy footsteps.

Quick as a splash of spray, the youth was in the branches. He hid himself above the pool which shone like a wet slate mirror. Motionless, he watched the ogress arrive with her two square buckets; he watched her kneel down with her necklace of small bones swinging. Then, before she could lean forward to dip and break the mirror surface, he showed his face reflected in the water.

"Huhn?" Tezlemokg grunted. She gaped down at the clear dark mirror. "I never knew I looked like that," she muttered. She glanced up into the tree, but saw only the green pine branches. She stared down at the pool again, and caught sight of the bright reflection.

"Huhn?" she grunted again, astounded. "I never knew before I was so pretty." She noticed the shimmering earrings. "I've got ear ornaments?" She fingered her big ears, puzzled. She glanced around, and above, then looked into the pool again, her stolid face becoming almost hopeful. "I never knew before I was so pretty." She smirked, and the face smiled at her; she frowned, and it frowned back at her. She felt of her ears again in simple wonder.

Then a wad of moss fell, shattering the lovely image.

Uttering a howl of rage and disappointment, Tezlemokg heaved herself up onto her giant feet and found a youth before her. She blinked at his dazzling brightness. Then she grabbed for him; but he darted aside, like a minnow in water.

"You cannot catch me, Tezlemokg," he teased her. "And even if you could, would it really help your beauty? Does eating children ever make you pretty?"

"I'll soon know that." She smacked her lips, betraying her wicked intentions. "I have some lovelies smoking."

The youth concealed an anxious frown. Then he smiled at the stupid ogress. "Are the children as handsome as I?" he slyly asked her.

"Mmmmm, no," she admitted. "What gives you so much beauty?"

"Magic," he answered lightly. "Strong medicine I carry." He flicked at one dazzling ear pendant until her eyes were fascinated by it. "Perhaps I carry my beauty in my ear ornaments," he suggested.

Tezlemokg moved to snatch them; but he flashed back from her hand as quick as a bouncing raindrop.

"Ah, ah," he warned, "you cannot take them from me. And even if you could, you could not wear such clusters of abalone. Your ears have not been pierced like a noble person's, with four holes in every earlobe. Even if I were to give you my glistening earbobs, how could you wear them to find out if they gave you beauty?" He cunningly moved his head to keep them all swinging slowly, and he watched her greedy eyes slither back and forth as she followed their lovely shimmer.

After some time she made an expected offer. "I'll pierce my ears," she told him.

"Yourself? How could you pierce your own ears? Why, truly the pain is dreadful. No, no, no, no. I shall keep my treasures." He managed to keep them gently swinging while giving her time to make a more foolish offer.

"You pierce them for me, boy," she at last suggested.

He pretended surprise. "Why should I pierce them for you? Besides, you could never stand it. Only noble-women, chiefs' nieces and wives and daughters, would have sufficient courage."

"Bah!" Tezlemokg's scorn filled the air like a clap of thunder. "I have more courage than a houseful of noble women. Give me your ear ornaments!" she demanded fiercely.

The youth sprang back to dodge her snatching fingers. "I may," he agreed, "when you are ready for them."

"Then make me ready, boy!" she roared down at him.

"Well . . ." He seemed to hesitate, to be reluctant. "Truly the pain is dreadful, and," he reminded her, "you are not noble. You have not a noble's courage."

"I will be noble when I have those piercings."

"But you're not noble yet, and so your courage . . ."

"Is greater than your own," she thundered at him. "You are afraid to do it."

"Well . . ." the youth admitted, "you're very big. And this could be just a trick. Perhaps, when I go near to pierce your ears, you'll reach out a hand and grab me."

"Bah!" Tezlemokg sneered. "If you're so scared, I'll let you tie my hands up. Yes, tie me and do it, coward!"

"If . . . you insist," the youth replied, frowning as if most unwilling.

"I do insist."

"Well then . . . we'll need rawhide ropes and . . . and sharpened spruce twigs for piercing and a stone hammer. I'm sure you have no hammer." Craftily, he seemed to resist the whole proceeding.

"Of course I have a hammer," she retorted. "And rope, and twigs. All in my lodge. So come on, boy! Come on and do it!"

"Well . . . if you insist." Appearing still most unwilling, he followed the ogress along the trail; he went into her dismal dwelling. There he saw the net hung high between two houseposts; he heard small children whimpering and coughing in the smoke from the rotten hemlock. One little form lay still. It seemed almost lifeless.

"Well, boy," stormed Tezlemokg, "why aren't you busy?"

"Those children," he gasped, as if fearing for his own safety.

"I like my children smoked like salmon," she informed him. "But have no fears for yourself. Just get to work!" She urged him to wrap her wrists, then to sharpen a pile of spruce twigs.

When the piercing sticks were ready, the youth still hesitated. "Lie . . . down," he suggested meekly.

Tezlemokg scowled down at him. "Lie down?" she objected. "Now, why should I lie down? Tell me!"

"Well how can I pierce your ears up there? And how can I drive twigs through without laying your lobes on something?"

The giantess thought it over. Then she lay down on some rough-hewn planking. "Now, come on boy!" she ordered.

"Wait till I tie your feet." He hesitated. "This may be just a trick. Perhaps you mean to grab me with your ankles."

"Bah! Tie my feet!" She let him tie both feet and hands securely. "Now, pierce my ears!" she thundered.

"If you insist," he said, and started working.

Although she shrieked with pain, she did hold still until two spikes were hammered in, one through each giant earlobe. Then Tezlemokg fainted, nailed fast to the heavy planking.

As quick as light, the youth was up a housepost. He cut one end of the net and, holding it, he flashed back to the floor again, tumbling the children out with soothing murmurs. He plastered grease on their eyes, softening the pitch that glued their lids together. Then, snatching up bits of salmon, he dipped it in oolaken grease and put it into their weakened fingers. He gave swift sips of water to all the children.

Bidal stirred just enough to take a few sips and whisper, "I want my mother."

"I'll take you to her at once," the youth assured her. Swooping her up, he hustled the captives out of their murky smokehouse.

Outside, the raven greeted them with a frenzy of joyous squawkings. Then he gurgled a signal, and two friendly black bears lumbered into the forest clearing.

"Thank you, Grandfather Raven," the youth said, with appreciation. He hoisted the children up onto shaggy backs of the black bears and whispered into their ears, "Hurry!" He stayed close to Bidal to see that she did not fall off. Then away they all went, past the pool that mirrored a slanting pine tree, and on and on and on through the great rain forest. There was need for haste since other ogres might free Tezlemokg.

Revived by the air and the water, Bidal clutched at the thick black fur and glanced around her. "Why, the forest isn't dark!" she breathed in wonder. A strange green light brightened everything about her; there were lovely dappled shadows on the trees and the lacy mosses. Then she noticed the shining youth and her eyes blinked, dazzled. He was as bright as the sun glimpsed through a morning sea mist. She sighed in pure delight at such radiant beauty, then she snuggled down on the bear and was lulled by his gentle jogging.

It was the swelling song of surf and sea gulls that roused her, and the voices of happy children.

"We're home, we're home, we're home!" all were wildly chanting.

The bears tumbled their riders off into springing mosses and ambled back through the forest. The raven whirred against the blue sky and flew over the village, screeching. And the people came running, shouting,

even weeping, in welcome.

Only one, Gundax, did not share in the happiness. Her sullen eyes seemed to wait with malicious patience.

"Bidal! Bidal!" The child heard her name breathed again and again and again by her thankful mother, and fond arms engulfed her in warmth and safety. Then Sudaol listened with the others to the tale of the children's rescue; she laughed with the rest at the trick on the wicked ogress.

Only one, Gundax, did not share in the merrymaking.

"You've done it now!" she whispered fiercely in Bidal's hearing. "Tezlemokg will be worse than ever!"

"I don't think so."

The shining youth had caught both Gundax's spiteful words and the alarmed look on the children's faces. "All Tezlemokg wants is beauty." He took off his glistening ear ornaments and held them out toward the watchful raven. "Give them to Tezlemokg," he ordered. "To Tezlemokg," he repeated, teasingly, since ravens are fond of keeping things that glitter.

The raven gave a disdainful squawk. Then, taking

the shimmering discs, he flew over the towering tree
tops.

The youth turned his clear blue eyes on Gundax as
though considering something. "Now I must leave,"
he announced, still eyeing her. From nowhere, it
seemed, he plucked a bow and arrows. Then, as the
village watched in awe, he loosed a flight of darts toward the blue sky. Up out of sight they flashed, each
like a shaft of concentrated sunbeams. More and more
arrows flew until at last the wondering people saw a
golden chain of arrows caught in the floor of Sky Land.

When the glittering chain had almost reached the
ground, the spirit boy fixed a stern eye on sullen Gundax.

"I have come to earth before, when I was needed,"
he said. His eyes narrowed, remembering some former
happening. "Once, when I came down to deal with
unkind people, I changed a man into an ugly dogfish."

Some children gasped. Gundax turned pale. And the
people stepped back in awe to leave a space around her.
All waited in breathless silence.

"Gundax might make a crab," he considered grimly.
"Always snapping at little children. Or a Devilfish,
perhaps?" He gazed hard at her as if contemplating
her vile potential. "Or a stinging ray?"

"Oh no, no, no!" shrieked Gundax, trembling with
terror. She fell to the ground before him in a torment
of pleading. "Oh no, no, no! Don't change me!"

"Then change yourself!" he ordered, and he leapt to
the chain of arrows. Up, up, up, up he flashed, up up

into radiant blueness.

"He may come back," wailed Gundax.

"So may Tezlemokg, too," whimpered little Bidal, remembering her own recent nightmare.

"Not any more," her mother assured her firmly. "The poor old ogress only wanted beauty. And now, with dazzling earrings, she'll be happy."

"Yes," breathed Bidal, with perfect understanding. "Perhaps she only wanted something pretty."

And so it seemed, for no one saw the wicked ogress again. She did not come again to Bidal's village. Sometimes at night, however, people thought they heard a wild triumphant "Ooo-ooo-eee-OOO" shrilling above the wind that tossed the pines and creaked the dismal cedars.

Once when they did, Bidal whispered, "Listen, Gundax! I think Tezlemokg sounds happy."

"Pffff!" scoffed the older girl. "Go to sleep, you stupid child! Don't be a nuisance!"

"Sh, sh," warned little Bidal. "Sh, sh, Gundax. Don't sound so cross or the shining one may hear you."

Gundax did shush. At once. And so, for Bidal, life was very happy.

Four

LIKE the wild woman of the woods, the cannibal giant was also an ogre known to most northwest Indians. The Tlingits, especially, have carved images of him.

Although the ancient legends about him varied from tribe to tribe, and his name was often different, usually it was the breaking of a taboo that brought on his visit. Invariably his end was the one told in this story.

According to the old way of thinking, any evil that befell had been brought by someone; it didn't just happen. Perhaps a man had flouted a sacred tribal custom, or a woman had angered the spirits of the river or mountain. And not until the offended spirits had been appeased, would the evil go from the people. In the old myths, it was often a girl who brought on the dread visit of the cannibal ogre.

There were strict laws about girls; many things were taboo. Usually, at about the age of thirteen years, girls were placed in seclusion either at the rear of a big house or in little brush huts at some distance from the village. In some tribes they stayed away for a whole year; in others only for about ten days of each month. At these times they were put in the care of an old grandmother and not allowed to mingle with other people. They were not allowed to look at living fish or at mountains since this might offend spirits. If they went out of doors, they had to cover their heads with large hoods.

Since to these ancient people the world was full of spirits, and since all spirits could either aid or harm humans, some individuals fasted and purified themselves until they became a medium for the spirits to work through. Such a person was called a shaman, an Indian medicine man. He used his spirit power mainly to cure the sick.

When a shaman became possessed by an evil spirit, however, and practiced wicked witchcraft to harm people, he was known as a sorcerer. He was then an outcast from society and was greatly feared by his village. People really believed he could kill them by witchcraft and so, perhaps because of their fear, his victims actually did die swiftly and strangely.

In this version of the cannibal giant legend, the sorcerer is Weedemris; the girl who breaks her taboo is Yaol, a princess of the Wolf Crest; the hero is Tawik, a common lad of the Frog Crest; and the ogre is Kloo-Teekl.

The Giant Ogre, Kloo-Teekl

ONCE UPON A TIME it happened that the handsomest, brightest boy in a northwest Indian tribe was a poor lad, Tawik, who lived in one of the Frog Crest houses. His tribal village stood at the end of a long sea arm thrust in among blue mountains.

Tawik was taller and more graceful than any of the highborn youths. This fact annoyed Gaa-kl, a scowling young Frog Crest noble. Tawik's arms were stronger, too; and when he paddled, his coppery skin rippled over his lissom muscles.

"But he can never captain a great canoe," muttered

Gaa-kl with satisfaction.

Tawik's hunter vision was keen. His eyes were as sharp as a diving sea hawk's.

"But he can never lead a hunting party," gloated Gaa-kl in scorn and malice.

Sometimes Tawik's eyes softened at sight of a slender girl, Yaol, who wore white sea-otter robes and glistening pearl ear ornaments. To him it seemed that her movements were as lovely as a sea gull's when it wheeled above a white seabeach.

"She is as beautiful as the birds," he whispered one day.

"And as high above you, Tawik," Gaa-kl reminded him, for Yaol was a Wolf Crest princess.

When she walked with her maidens, Tawik would steal a glance at her. Then he would sigh and slip away, his shoulders slumping. For he was of common birth, and in the old days along the northwest coast, hereditary rank was most important. A common youth could never win a princess. In fact, he could not hope to have her slightest notice.

Yet Tawik hoped.

"Some day," he wistfully confided to a sea gull, "perhaps she will forget to sing when she is picking berries; and an offended grizzly bear will rear up right before her. I will hear her screams and rush to grapple with him. I will die, saving the lovely princess. And she will weep for me."

"Or, perhaps," he told a raven, "some day when we are traveling far out at sea, coming home from the halibut fish camp, a shark or a sea lion will attack Yaol's canoe. She'll be capsized, but I will leap into the water and draw the brute away from her. Later, perhaps, she will think of me and remember I died to save her."

He dreamed of slaying bears and wolves and devilfish to save the princess and win a grateful thought from her. Always his brave dreams let him die since, living, he could not have her. He hovered about Yaol from a respectful distance, yet somehow he never chanced to catch the sighs and glances she in turn bestowed on him.

Only three people noticed: Gaa-kl, his uncle Weedemris, and the wise old Frog-House-Chiefmother.

Chiefmother, an old and noble lady, watched the young pair with kindly disapproval. She wished she could help Tawik, but ancient custom was the sacred law of every Indian village. Nobles and common folk could never marry. That was the law, and to break that—or any—law was to court disaster.

"He is such a faithful lad," she sighed. "His spirit is noble, if his blood is common." It saddened her to know that Tawik could never rise above his humble station. He could not become a chief or a leader among sea-hunters, nor could he carve a pole with ancient emblems. Such honored work belonged to highborn clansmen, as did the cherished names. Only a great shortage of nobles ever provided a chance for such a boy to rise, and there was no shortage in the Frog Crest houses. So Frog-House Chiefmother sympathized in silence. She also kept an eye on old Weedemris. He was a man to fear.

Weedemris was a wily sorcerer. Once a famous shaman, he had worn his crown of grizzly bear claws with honor, and had shaken his medicine rattle for many years to drive off harmful spirits. Now, however, he was possessed by an evil spirit. With his scraggly hair falling down about his knees, he danced frightening, frenzied dances; and he terrified the village with his deathbox. People knew he need only put one hair of theirs into his dreadful deathbox and, as certain as night and day, the victim's death would follow.

Often his eyes followed Tawik, as he looked at Yaol.

Chiefmother knew why. The sorcerer wanted the Wolf Clan princess for his nephew, Gaa-kl.

The old woman knew what would soon happen. The sorcerer would ask for Yaol in marriage for his nephew, and the Wolf chiefs would scarcely dare oppose him. If they should do so, they would be in deadly danger. If Tawik stood in the witchdoctor's way, he would be dealt with also; a hair from his glossy head might go into the fearful deathbox.

Finally the time was near when the Wolf clan would begin to plan for the princess's marriage.

Tawik knew it as well as his wise Chiefmother. For almost a year the princess had been secluded for part of each moon. She was living now with her maidens and an old woman in a small brush hut at the foot of a timbered mountain, some distance behind the village. When she came out again, her family must arrange a proper marriage for her. What was to be, would be. "I cannot push back the tide, nor fight the wind," thought Tawik.

Yet his heart was as heavy as an anchorstone one day as he paddled down river with a catch of salmon. It was spring. Along the banks the cottonwood trees were bursting their sticky leaf buds. Young leaves were golden green with captured sunlight. The world was lovely and new again, but Yaol was hidden from it, preparing herself for marriage. A curl of smoke rose up from a stand of spruce to reveal her prison.

Before a bend in the river could hide it from view, Tawik glanced back to see the lonely smoke-curl. And then he saw something else that filled his mind with horror. A blood red whiff of smoke! It belched up from behind a mountain, far up river.

"Kloo-Teekl!" he gasped. "The smoke from Kloo-Teekl's fire!"

Kloo-Teekl was the dread of every inland traveler, a cannibal giant whose nose stretched out at night to become a sharp proboscis that sucked the blood of humans.

"Kloo-Teekl will see her smoke there in the spruces!" Tawik thought. Alarmed, he swung his canoe about. Then he stopped it in consternation.

He dared not rescue Yaol.

The seclusion of girls was, of all things, most sacred. Men were taboo, and to go against a taboo was to anger spirits. Angered spirits might guide Kloo-Teekl to the secluded princess; whereas, if all laws were obeyed, the spirits might help protect her. The danger might pass without her ever knowing.

Yet . . .

Her smoke was a clear blue signal. Kloo-Teekl was sure to see it.

Someone must warn her, swiftly.

In an instant, he put about toward the village. He would give the alarm so the women could come and save her. Exerting his fiercest strength, he sent his slim craft slicing through the water. Yaol's very life rested now on his flashing paddle.

As he drew near the village, he sensed a commotion in it. People were gathered in anxious groups; work lay about unheeded. Perhaps they already knew about the ogre. With one last paddle plunge, he swept the canoe up to the beach. Then he leapt swiftly toward Chiefmother.

"Kloo-Teekl," he panted. "Hurry . . . to Yaol! Hurry!"

Her eyes went wide with fright. She seemed startled by his disclosure, so it must be something else that stirred the village. The boy's glance of inquiry brought him an instant answer.

It was Yaol. She had broken her sacred taboo. She had looked at the mountains, offending their guardian spirits.

"In the seclusion hut," Chiefmother explained, "when Yaol's maidens teased her about Gaa-kl, she burst into tears and rushed out with her head un-covered." The shocked woman guard had rushed to

the village to tell the Wolf Chiefs about it; and being a gossip, she had babbled to many others. "Now the whole tribe fills the air with lamentations."

Tawik knew what they feared. Yaol had offended the spirits; now her village would suffer vengeance. To break an ancient law was to bring disaster.

"And Kloo-Teekl has come already," Chiefmother breathed in awe. She accepted the ogre's arrival as a just, if swift, retribution.

"But she may not be to blame," Tawik objected hotly. "Perhaps she looked at no hills, Chiefmother." He glared at his gossiping tribesmen with defiance. "Yet they will blame her for Kloo-Teekl's coming."

"When they find out," the woman agreed. She frowned as she thought about it.

"Oh hurry, Chiefmother, please!" begged Tawik. "Kloo-Teekl will see her smoke. Her hut fire must be put out quickly."

"But not by you, good lad. I will go to her Wolf Chiefmother."

The lad's anxious gaze followed her until she disappeared into the largest of the Wolf Crest houses. Then he waited impatiently until she reappeared with a group of young Wolf Crest women. He saw them all make straight for a Wolf canoe and paddle away, up river. How he wished they would travel faster!

Meanwhile Tawik himself was watched. Weedemris observed him with a burning hatred, for he knew why the girl had found Gaa-kl distasteful. She preferred a common youth to his noble nephew. Her foolish act had smeared shame on his favorite; it had marked Gaa-kl as an unwelcome suitor.

Blood! Only blood could wipe such shame off Gaa-kl. And not just common blood, for a noble youth was worth three common persons.

Unaware of old Weedemris, Tawik stayed watching the river with impatience. They would bring the princess and her maidens back to the safety of the Wolf House, surely!

Yet when the Wolf craft returned, it brought only four hooded maidens.

"Just four?" thought Tawik, startled. He was scanning the girls' dark fur robes.

"The princess would not come," his Chiefmother confided, pausing briefly beside the tall lad. "She says she broke her taboo, so she will wait by herself for vengeance. She will not draw spirit wrath toward the tribe or village. And you, Tawik," the old woman warned, "you must draw no anger either!"

"I will do nothing rash," he promised. "Nothing to anger spirits. But is her smoke still rising above those spruces?"

"Her fire is out."

"And Kloo-Teekl's fire?"

"Is where it was. Perhaps he will not come across the mountains."

And so it seemed.

Whole days went by without his moving closer. He did not come, yet did not leave the country. Weeks went by, and still the red smoke drifted, a never ending threat to every person.

"Why does he not go away?" wailed the worried women.

"Perhaps he waits for the Moon of Berries," Gaa-kl suggested, since the tribal berry patch spreads near the spot where the smoke was rising.

"Perhaps," the women gasped, now really shaken. They raised angry fists toward the hut of the Wolf Crest princess. It was all her fault that this evil had come upon them. She had broken a taboo, but the whole village was being punished.

"Or perhaps the cannibal waits for goat hunting time," Gaa-kl suggested one day to the men whose tribal hunting grounds stretched through those menaced mountains.

"Perhaps," the men agreed, their eyes bright with fury.

"He will rouse them until they strike," Tawik muttered in consternation. "It is his way of revenge."

And so it seemed, for Gaa-kl continued to prick the people.

"How shall we catch the salmon runs?" he asked, knowing well that the tribe's finest fishing stations were far up river, near the rushing mountain canyons.

"We will not starve," Tawik burst out. "We could live on sea food forever."

"And tell me, then, my bold but common clansman," Gaa-kl retorted, "what we shall offer at the inter-tribal trading if we do not hunt goat and gather berries. What shall we give in return for Haida canoes? For

Tlingit copper? For fish grease from the Nishga people?"

A score of faces darkened at this question. Tradition demanded dried berry cakes, goat kidney fat, and goat horns from this village. Without these time honored items, the tribe not only would be shamed, it would also be unable to trade for the things it needed.

"How shall we buy gifts for the chiefs' potlatches?" continued Gaa-kl. "Or shall we fail to give them?"

"We will be shamed along the coast." A murmur rose among the people, and once again they shook their fists toward the offending princess.

"Spirits have not guided Kloo-Teekl to her hut," Tawik reminded them. "Surely she must be blameless!" But his words were lost; they were drowned in a great wave of roaring anger.

Gaa-kl, his work accomplished, slipped down the long sea arm one night in search of a bride at some other village. Before he left, he talked long with his wicked uncle.

"Weedemris is planning something," thought Tawik in anguish. He was tempted to swoop the princess up and take her away to safety. But to go near her hut, breaking more taboos, would certainly bring on more trouble. Kloo-Teekl had not attacked; the spirits might still protect her if no one offended further. But he watched Weedemris, carefully. This was a danger he might combat.

One night Tawik saw the witchdoctor's three wizened wives steal through the moonlight to paddle down the sea arm. What they were seeking, he could not discover; but he watched the grisly group with increasing sharpness.

Meanwhile the hunters just sat and waited. Tawik watched them, too.

"We will be shamed if we sit here like quivering aspens," he scoffed, to draw their thinking from the princess. "We must drive this ogre from our land or be known as unworthy people."

At first no one listened to his brave words. But then there were pow-wows and earnest councils. And at last it was agreed that the ogre must be hunted or the village would be shamed.

Men ventured in hunting parties. Tawik went with them into the mountains where they found the husks of bears and wolves and mountain goats, sucked dry of blood and tossed off like a heap of clamshells.

Then they heard a triumphant bellow.

Kloo-Teekl had caught the scent of human beings.

Shrinking inside with fear, the hunters closed in upon the awful ogre; but their spears glanced off his skin; their arrows bounced back like hailstones. The hunters became the hunted.

Again and again they ventured into the mountains, but always the group came back with hunters missing. And still the ogre lived. Great seats became empty in all the big cedar lodges; many mats were sadly lifted from the long sleeping platforms. But the menace remained.

The tribe at last decided it would have to leave its

old and handsome village. It would have to forsake its forefather's goat hunting grounds; it would have to forget its ancient salmon fishing stations. It would slink away, with its old pride gone forever.

"Because of a stupid princess," people muttered.

"Perhaps the spirits are angry because we have failed to punish her for offending the mountain spirits."

Like a rising storm, village anger swirled again around the secluded princess.

"Let us sharpen a snag," they cried, "and impale the Wolf princess on it!"

"Lash her to the beach," they yelled, "and let the high tide take Yaol!"

Tawik blanched with fear for her and considered a rash rescue, but always his Chiefmother stayed him. "Patience, good lad," she cautioned.

Wolf shamans did what they could to save their princess. They chanted and danced; they shook ancient charms and rattles; but the giant stayed where he was. There was nothing else to do. Yaol must be sacrificed to the angry mountain spirits, or the ogre would stay forever, and the people must leave their village.

In one last effort to avert the sacrifice, the Wolf chiefs approached Weedemris. He had been a mighty shaman, they all remembered. He still had dreadful power and potent magic. Perhaps, if they humored him, he would turn his skills against the awful ogre. Perhaps he would save Yaol for his nephew Gaa-kl.

"What can be done?" they asked him very humbly.

In Weedemris's evil eyes a triumph glittered. It was

as if he had planned and waited for this moment. "I will climb into the sky and see what can be done," he slyly offered.

"He has a plan, Chiefmother," whispered Tawik. A coldness seemed to wrap him like a sea fog. "He has a plan, Chiefmother."

"Well, you have eyes to watch," she answered sharply. "That is still your task, Tawik, to watch and watch and watch him!"

And Tawik watched, his eyes keen as a diving sea hawk's.

First the sorcerer placed a wooden puppet in the largest of the Frog Crest houses. It was a small image of a female shaman that he often used because, he said, a spirit voice spoke through it, the voice of his great-great-great-grandmother.

Then he lay down on a mat nearby and fell into a trance while his soul left his body to climb into the sky in search of guidance. When it returned to him, he rose up slowly and donned his crown of grizzly bear claws. Around his skinny form he tied a leather apron fringed with the dried clattering beaks of many dead sea puffins. He picked up his charms and rattle. Then, while medicine drums throbbed through the shadowy lodge, he leapt about the fire, chanting weird incantations.

The four clans of the tribe glided in on their bare feet. They waited, silent, for the sorcerer's verdict.

Suddenly, Weedemris stood still and listened. He raised one bony finger. Then he pointed to the wooden puppet.

The people hushed to hear its words of wisdom. Even the drums fell silent. All waited for the spirit guidance.

The puppet seemed to speak in a voice that was thin and wavering, like the voice of an old, old woman:

"Fire! Only by fire can Kloo-Teekl be killed by humans!"

People drew back in awe as the spirit spoke—all but Tawik. His watchful eyes had caught some preparations. A long kelp tube led to the wooden puppet.

It stretched from a corner where the sorcerer's three wives were lurking. That had been the old hags' moon-lit catch; kelp tubes that were long enough to reach from the corner to the wooden puppet. A kelp bulb, sliced across, was a speaking funnel.

"Fire! Only by fire can Kloo-Teekl be killed by humans!" The witchdoctor's chanted words picked up the puppet's. The drums took up the beat. Shamans joined the witchdoctor's dance with charms and rattles. People dared to hope again. They smiled, and their shoulders lifted.

Only Tawik remained alert and grim and wary. He knew the sorcerer's plan had only started, and it boded no good to the girl who had scorned his nephew.

All the tribal chiefs and leading men, impressed by the spirit voice, at once began to plan the ogre's burning. At last they had spirit aid to guide their actions.

They planned to deepen the pit they used for catching grizzly bears. They would strengthen its entangling net with fresh sea-lion rawhide and conceal the pit with extra brush and large ferns. They would have to bait the trap, of course, and entice Kloo-Teekl to it. Then, instead of lurking nearby with spears and clubs as they did when they were bear-hunting, they would hide in a cave with pitch torches and piles of brushwood. One man would watch the pit and give the rest a signal. When Kloo-Teekl fell, the lone guard would blast his whistle. Then all would rush out at once and burn the captured giant.

"How shall we bait the trap?"

In the hush that followed came the puppet's answer.

"Princess Yaol must be the bait."

Tawik sprang to his feet but a hand stayed him.

"Patience, good lad!" commanded his Chiefmother.

"But I will be the bait," he offered. "Gladly!"

The woman shook her head, then whispered to him, "When spirits have spoken, do not go against them!"

"Spirits?" he hissed. "An old wife with a kelp tube!"

"The people would not believe you. And if they did, they would not thwart old Weedemris. They fear to draw his wrath upon themselves. You know that, Tawik."

He did know that. Tawik scowled in futile rage and slumped his shoulders.

"Patience," Chiefmother said, "and you may yet save the princess. With hunters scarce, I can arrange for you to be the one who guards the pit and gives the burning signal. The rest is up to you. Remember, though, Kloo-Teekl must be killed. Your duty to your tribe comes first and foremost."

"My duty will be done," said Tawik simply.

"At the dark of the moon Kloo-Teekl burns!" the sorcerer's voice was chanting.

That was two nights ahead. Tawik had just two days to think of something. It was no simple thing, this time, like killing a grizzly or drawing away a sea beast. He would need sharp wits to out trick a prince of tricksters. And the threat was real, not valiant fancy. Yaol's life was in his hands.

When he lay down that night, his prayers leapt

toward the sky with the licking lodgefire; they rose
with the smoke toward Raven, the Chief of Tricksters.

"Send me your spirit power, supernatural Raven!
Send me your spirit aid," he entreated humbly.

For hours he tossed and turned, and tossed and
turned, awaiting a spirit vision. Then, when at last he
slept, a vivid dream came to him.

In his dream the sorcerer's puppet became the Wolf
Crest princess. Its shaman regalia was replaced by
sea-otter garments; its crackling old voice became
Yaol's soft sobbing.

Tawik woke with a start. That was the trick he
would use. He would copy Weedemris's cunning with
a kelp tube and wooden image. He would replace the
living bait with a wooden princess image. Exhilerated
by his idea, he remembered a certain log that was
punky and light and crumbling. He could roughly
shape it with an adze and fishknife. Chiefmother
would give him the proper fur robes to clothe it.

Excitedly he planned the many details. He would
lash the image to a pole so that it would look like the
real princess lashed to a pole across the deadly bear
pit. He would scent the wooden image with furs fresh
from Chiefmother's person. He would attach a long
kelp tube, a kelp tube with a speaking funnel. Then,
when he had switched the poles, he would hide the
princess where she would not be seen or scented by the
monster. She would sob through the speaking funnel,
and her voice would carry along the tube and seem to
come from the wooden image.

It pleased Tawik to use the sorcerer's own special trick for his undoing. Then it frightened him to think that his was a lesser cunning. The trick might fail when performed by a clumsy novice.

If it did fail, then he himself would leap out on the pole to lure Kloo-Teekl. He would die, if need be, to save the princess.

For two days he worked in stealth, helped by Chief-mother, and watched by her as well. It seemed as if she, too, were plotting something; as if she, too, had a secret purpose to accomplish.

As the evening of the second day fell, all was ready. Yaol lay across the pit and the men stood watching and listening. Tawik was seized then with sudden fear. He was ready, too, but he knew his trick would fail. He would not have time enough to switch the two poles. He shuddered as he saw the living princess lashed to a pole across the deadly bear pit. It was hard to wait, and yet he must. He had to wait until the men had gone.

He waited and then a startled lift of sleeping birds announced Kloo-Teekl's coming. The men scurried caveward to kindle their burning-torches. It was time.

With hammering heart, Tawik tied a rope to one end of the bait-pole. He tossed the rope up over a strong pine branch to give him leverage. Pulling frantically, he lifted the pole as if it were a hinged lid over the bear pit.

He heard a rock dislodged by Kloo-Teekl's footfall, coming closer.

Swallowing his dread, he pulled on a hidden rope and dragged the wooden image across the bear pit.

"Hurry!" the princess begged, still lashed to the suspended log. "Hurry, hurry!" Then she wailed again, as she had been told, to lure the ogre to her.

"Courage, Princess," Tawik urged. He slashed her bonds and caught her falling body; he kicked the pole away, and cut the rope that held it. Then, swooping

the princess up, he carried her to the hollow tree where the kelp mouthpiece was waiting.

"Cry out," he said, "as if for help. Sob and scream for your maidens, Princess!"

Faint with relief, Yaol gave him a grateful glance and started screaming. Carried along the tube, her voice rose loudly from the wooden image.

"It works!" breathed Tawik.

Around them the gloomy night lay on the forest. Only the baited pit was lighted by the silver starlight. Tawik moved from the hollow tree, creeping softly toward the bear trap. What if Kloo-Teekl should know? Almost breathless with fear, he awaited the monster's coming.

Suddenly, the cannibal emerged, big as a grizzly bear and more heart-stopping.

A sharper scream rose from the brush and big ferns.

Kloo-Teekl stopped; then leapt ahead, his proboscis like a hurtling spear. He crashed down through the brush and ferns, and was impaled on the image.

Tawik blasted the signal.

Men rushed from the cave with flaming torches and piles of brushwood. They heaped fire on the monster, but he only yelled through its crackling.

"Mere humans cannot kill the supernatural!"

Through four long days and nights the flames kept leaping, until only hot ashes were smoking deep in the bear pit. To be quite sure of Kloo-Teekl's death, men took long poles to stir up the smouldering cinders. And as they stirred, a roaring twisting wind rose, swirling up from the pit in a funnel of zooming ashes. And as it rose, each bit of ash took wings; each sprouted a small probiscis; each roared about the men like a tiny ogre.

The cannibal, Kloo-Teekl, had become earth's first mosquitoes, for humans can not kill the supernatural.

Neither can they escape its angry vengeance. For as the people watched agape, the mosquitoes thrust ahead like a huge black arrow. Gathering their forces, they made straight for Weedemris who fled before their wrath into the forest. He never again came to the village.

Though they sighed with relief, the Wolf clansmen now mourned for their young princess. It was sad, they thought, that one so young and lovely had been so used.

But Frog Chiefmother was not sad. She called the four clans of the tribe into the Frog feasthouse for a joyous potlatch. She offered all who came both food and entertainments. And then at last she brought out the Wolf Crest princess. She told them the story of Tawik and his wooden image. All together, Wolves and Bears, Eagles and Frogs rejoiced, and all praised Tawik warmly.

Then the Frog Chief handed his speaker's staff to one who sadly recounted all the Frog Clan's losses in the fight against Kloo-Teekl. "Great names are empty now, with none to wear them," he said. "We must choose common men of worth and elevate them."

The Chief beckoned to Tawik to come and stand before him. He gave him the ancient honored name of Az-jex, and he placed Az-jex regalia on the lad, thus claiming that name's high rank for the boy who had saved the princess.

The four clans of the tribe witnessed the claim with joy and made it legal.

"Now, we must arrange a proper marriage for you," said Chiefmother, smiling brightly.

And Tawik was glad he had not died saving the lovely Yaol.

Five

THE FIFTH and longest legend, "Fly Again, My Proud Eagle," is an historical adventure, based firmly on actual happenings. Princess Da-ul, who escaped massacre at Kitsum-galum to preserve the Eagle dynasty, was as real and as romantic a figure as Bonnie Prince Charlie. Her son, Prince Hayis, living in the Haida islands, was as wrongfully deprived of his rights as was Robin Hood living in Sherwood Forest, or as was Richard the Lion Hearted. His return to Kitsumgalum was in the knightly tradition.

Some knowledge of the ancient Indian laws of inheritance is necessary, however, for an appreciation of the story.

Although rules of lineage varied somewhat among the Tsimshian, Tlingit, and Haida peoples, a boy (or a girl) belonged to his mother's clan and tribe and nation. He inherited the name, rank, totems, and privileges of his mother's brother, and not of his father. Mainly he was trained by his maternal uncles.

Since members of a clan believed themselves related (because of common traditions tracing back to the same origin), they were not allowed to intermarry. So every household contained members of two clans:

the father in one, the mother and children in another.

Because of this system, it was Princess Da-ul, and not a royal prince, who was helped to escape when the Eagle Clan of Kitsum-galum was slaughtered by the Bear Clan of the same tribe. She carried the royal bloodline. And it was her eldest son, Hayis, who became "crown prince" of the Tsimshian Eagles.

The lodges of the Kitsum-galums were situated on the mainland, on a tributary of the Ksan River (Skeena River). Prince Hayis's birthplace, a Haida village, was on one of the big islands that lie well offshore, across a turbulent stretch of water.

More than their rightful royal claims drew Prince Hayis and his brothers and one sister across the treacherous sea. There was also their sacred duty: their duty to the ghosts of their murdered clansmen, and their duty to the prestige of their Eagle Totem.

According to their beliefs, the welfare of the dead depended mainly on the acts of the living. The souls of the murdered hovered in the air, they thought, like drifting logs, until their wrongs had been wiped out by vengeance. Only revenge would free the ghosts to go on to the happy Land of Souls or to return to tribal life through reincarnation.

Too, pride and shame were mighty forces among these Indian peoples. Only revenge could lift the heads of a wronged (and so, shamed) group of people. The honor of their Totem was as precious to them as the free fluttering of our flag is to us.

Fly Again, My Proud Eagle

ONCE, near the end of a long and bitterly cold winter, starvation stalked the Tsimshian lodges like a hungry wolf. At Kitsum-galum, only the wealthy Eagle Clan was left with enough provisions.

"And we have barely enough," old Eagle Chief Neeswana protested to his envious neighbors. "We have barely enough to give us strength for the journey northward."

The only hope of survival that year was to follow the ancient Grease Trail north to the Nass River to harvest the oolaken run there.

The Nass—or Nishga—tribes were a friendly branch of the Tsimshian Nation, so they would lease fishing stations to their starving cousins, and fishing gear, and huts to shelter them from the cold blasts.

"The Eagles alone will reach the Nass," muttered Wigad, a wily sorcerer of the hungry Bear Clan. He sought the willing ear of the Bear Chief, Saxsaxt. "The Eagles will reach the Nass and harvest the fish, while the Bears die in icy snowdrifts. Unless . . ."

"Unless?" asked Saxsaxt, inviting him to continue.

"Unless the Bears choose to live."

Saxsaxt narrowed his eyes, considering. Then he surveyed the handsome lodges owned by the mighty Eagles. "The Bears will choose to live," he decided grimly.

That night a group of Bear Clan warriors fell on the sleeping Eagles, and murdered the fighting men. Then, in a fierce battle that raged for two nights and one day, they slaughtered the Eagle people.

Only the eldest Eagle princess, Da-ul, escaped with her grandfather, old Eagle Chief Neeswana. And she tried to turn back to search for her younger sister.

"I'm sure Wineeks is alive," she insisted to her grandfather. "That small owl's hoot we heard coming from the pine thicket—that was Wineeks, I know. Oh, please, Grandfather, can't we turn back and search that thicket for her?"

"No," Neeswana answered firmly. He forced the sobbing girl ahead, north, through the mountain passes. "If we turned back, Da-ul, we would not live to come this way again."

"Better to die," she flung at him. "Better to die with her than to escape, knowing I failed my sister . . . knowing I might have saved her."

"You have a greater thing to save," Neeswana reminded Da-ul. "Escaping, you save the royal bloodline."

". . . and hear my little sister . . . forever . . . calling in vain to me."

Neeswana's dark eyes blazed at his granddaughter. "And would you rather hear forever the spirits of our dead kinsmen wailing in vain for vengeance? Would you rather hear forever the voices of the Eagle Clan lamenting their fallen glory? Let me speak once of this, and only once! You wear the great name, Da-ul. You carry the highest Tsimshian chieftainship in trust for future Eagles. While you still live, the Bear has not slaughtered the mighty Eagle. If Saxsaxt should capture you and kill you, the Eagle is brought low indeed; and Eagle clansmen in all the tribes will bow their heads at feasts while Bears flaunt captured royal Eagle crests and songs and dances. The shame of that!" He shuddered.

"But . . . little Wineeks . . ."

"Little Wineeks would wish you courage to do your duty. She knows the Clan planned your escape a long, long time ago; and she knows why they planned it. Like your brothers and uncles, she will die comforted by the assurance that the Eagle will fly again. She knows that a princess's heart must beat for all her clan,

not for herself and her own nearest dear ones. That is the royal burden. We will not speak of this again. You know your duty, Da-ul."

The princess hugged her white weasel robes about her shivering body. She gazed south longingly, only once. Then, facing the cold north wind, she lifted her weary feet and plodded on, on, on through the mountain passes. Snowflakes fell on her glossy black braids. Wind tugged at her furs and clattered her pearly earrings. But she made no complaint.

"The Eagle will fly again," she vowed, trudging on through the endless snowdrifts.

At last, at long last, they reached the Nass and turned westward toward the sea. Cold blasts of bitter wind tore at their clothes like hungry beasts and then howled on through the bare tree branches. Numbed by her grief, fainting with hunger, and weary with endless plodding, Da-ul felt as bleak and lonely as the shrouded white world around her.

Then they came to Fishery Bay. The water was clear of ice; it teemed with life and movement. People were gathered by the thousands to harvest the oolakan run at ancestral fishing stations.

"Welcome, Princess!" Nishga Eagles called out to the sad faced girl, though they had no time to serve her.

"Welcome, Princess!" Nishga Wolves hailed her, thinking perhaps they might arrange a marriage with the forlorn yet regal maiden. But marriage arrangements, too, had to wait on the precious fish run.

Their welcome warmed her heart. The noisy excitement stirred her, like returning springtime.

Silver shoals of tiny oolaken were moving from the deep salt sea into the northern river, pursued by a churning of hungry hair seals and ravenous sea lions. The bay was sliced by countless dorsal fins of killer whales. And above the sea, the very air itself seemed to scream with a million sea gulls.

Wistfully she watched agile canoemen rake in the precious silver while people rushed about feeding the fires that heated their cooking stones. Forlornly remembering other harvest times, she admired the skill with which Nishga women sorted mountains of fish for drying or for oil pressing. They strung tiny fish on lines and spiralled them about tall groups of poles, where they hung like icicles.

"Oolaken trees," she murmured. She wished she could be a part of it; busy, absorbed, and losing herself in the roaring, clattering, swirling, screeching harvest. But this was not to be for a royal princess.

"Stay in the fishing hut!" Neeswana commanded sternly. "It is not seemly for you to walk about unattended by slaves or maidens."

"But . . . I have no slaves, Grandfather. I have no maidens either."

"You have your dignity," he snapped, "and your duty to ancient custom."

So, sighing with disappointment, Da-ul stayed in seclusion. It seemed to her, and indeed it was true, that she alone had no work. And some had too much.

In all the clattering hubbub around the fishing camp, three little ones were drowned.

"Three tiny Eagles," Da-ul said mourning. "Why can't I watch the children? Surely caring for little Eagles is part of my royal duty?"

Neeswana consented and the Nishgas were grateful and understanding. They arranged for Da-ul to take a group of tiny girls into an ancient playhouse. This was a huge hollow log, enormous at its sealed, root end, and bleached silver by sun and wind. Down through the years, the open end had been well closed, a fireplace built inside, a good smokehole arranged, and a portal hole made for entry. Now, mothers provisioned it with food and fuel, fur robes and sleeping mats. "We will come every morning to kindle the fire," they promised.

Glad to be occupied, Da-ul tended her charges gently. "I have my maidens now," she told Neeswana. She found joy in their merry ways and in their little round brown faces.

Once, when she walked with her girls, a Wolf Chief approached Da-ul to give her his nephew's eagle. It was a young bird that had been injured and made a pet of.

"The eagle is in your care," he said, with double meaning. "And under your care, Da-ul, the eagle will fly again." He glanced with hope toward his handsome nephew.

"You will soon fly again," Da-ul promised the dark young eagle, flexing its great wing gently. She stroked its glistening feathers that had not yet picked up their brighter glint of copper, and fondled the proud head that was not yet as white as the mountain peaks around her. And she gave him a name, "Young Eagle."

Young Eagle stayed with the princess, perching high on the root-gnarl of her drifted log, as though cresting a royal housepole. With regal grace, he surveyed the swirling harvest.

The oolaken run was at its peak when a freak tide struck the fish camp—perhaps from some deep disturbance. Always along the northwest coast, the tide rise is tremendous. But the log had lain for years above the tide, silvered and safe where some wild storm had tossed it. Da-ul noticed no sign of danger before she and her children went to bed that evening. On this night, however, the water rose far higher than it had ever come. And people rose the next morning to find that the log had vanished; the log, Da-ul, the girls, and even the faithful eagle, all were gone.

The Nishgas were lost in wonder. They thought some supernatural force, evil or good, had taken the Eagle princess. Aghast at their loss, parents huddled with anxious whispers, remembering dreadful ancient stories.

"It was bewitched, that log," a few old women muttered. "Evil Wigad must have cast a spell on it."

All the Nishga Eagles gazed west, toward the open sea, and their mournful wails rose with the sea gulls' screaming. They searched, of course, but found no trace of their loved ones.

Only Neeswana appeared to be untroubled. "The Eagle will fly again," he kept repeating. Perhaps he thought that the Sky Chief's son or the supernatural Chief Killer Whale had sheltered the precious princess. Perhaps he believed she would return some day with supernatural children.

When the tide took the log, Da-ul was sleeping soundly. So were her tiny charges. They were snugly asleep, their rabbit robes around them. And all slept late the next morning, lulled by the gentle motion.

When Da-ul awoke, she wondered at the motion. Lifting her head, she glanced through the portal hole and saw strange misted mountains. Scrambling to see still more, she thrust her tousled head out. Rocks rushed toward her. Islands slid by. The gray sea moved about her. Her log was drifting swiftly, as if caught in a tiderip or sped by a great sea current. Kelp heads bobbed all around, trailing their sea-brown tresses. Tangles of kelp tubes twisted like brown sea serpents; and the fins of killer whales sliced through the water.

"I'm hungry, Princess," she heard a small voice saying.

"Of course you are," she said in a soothing manner.

Da-ul stirred the cold gray ashes, trying to find one spark of living fire; but there was none. So she sought the fire-drill, giving out strips of fat, meanwhile, to keep her small girls happy. They must not know they were adrift, at least not yet, not until things looked much more cheerful.

"Cac, cac, cac, cac!"

"Young Eagle!" Da-ul was relieved to hear his loud clear call from his perch on the floating root-gnarl.

"Cac, cac, cac, cac!"

She translated it for her charges. "He says to stay inside today and listen to my stories. Now watch me make the fire!"

Unused to menial tasks, she did it badly and had many painful blisters; but at last a flame leapt warmly, lighting the drifting shelter. Smoke rose up through its smokehole, wafting a wistful signal. And the long day passed with quiet songs and stories.

Only when night came did dreadful fears come crowding. What if they drifted far out to hostile islands? What if a storm came up and splintered the log on some bare reef?

Da-ul crept to the portal hole to offer a sacrifice to the storm spirits of the sea. She meant to offer food, but thinking about the children, she offered instead one of her lustrous ear ornaments.

What if they caught, like snags, out on a hungry sandbar? Or what if they drifted out to the giant whirlpool that sucked everything down, out where the ocean ended? Or to supernatural regions: to the Land of Chief Pestilence, or to the country where dwarfs and fierce birds were warring? With trembling respect, Da-ul offered another earring.

Morning came at last. It was blue and white, all bathed in a sparkling sunshine. Behind her, distant and far, the mountains and rain forests were blue. Around her the sea was blue, deep blue and shining. Above her the sky was blue, blue with white clouds.

Da-ul's heart lifted. Then it dropped in a sudden panic, for the sea heaved with a strange new motion. Slow and majestic its great waves came, the swells of the North Pacific. Their size and power alarmed the girl, accustomed as she was to lakes and rivers. The log, she knew, had drifted far out to sea.

"I'm hungry, Princess," she heard a small voice saying.

"Of course you are," she answered. "Poor little things," she thought, "all trusting me completely."

She told them then that they were all adrift, but that help would be coming. Somehow she kept them warmed and fed and happy. She gathered rainfall when the weather changed; and days went by, and dreadful nights. And always Young Eagle perched high on the root-gnarl, using his wings at times to fish for his simple supper.

One night the sun went down with streaks of flaming color, leaving the sea finally all dark and gray and lonely. Trembling with fear, Da-ul offered the storm spirits and the dread sea-monsters the last of her crested bracelets and all but the last of her lustrous ear ornaments. Then she fell asleep, exhausted.

She woke to find sunlight streaming through the portal hole and smokehole, and the log motionless. Were they stuck on a reef? A hungry sandbar? Slowly she crept toward the golden sunbeams.

"Trees! Rocks! A beach white with broken clam-shell!" Then she saw several big fishing lodges. "Haida or Tlinget?" Da-ul wondered. Either could be unfriendly.

Waking the children gently, she told them to stay well hidden until she returned. Then, shivering with fear, she smoothed her long black hair, lifted her chin, and walked out on the strange beach proudly.

She saw the canoes, Haida canoes proudly wearing their Haida emblems. Da-ul swallowed with consternation. These great carved clipper craft carried their sea-roving owners over the stormy waters to fish, sea-hunt, and raid. They raided for slaves and slave wives. His heart thudded under his weasel robe, but she moved on with the stately grace that best became a Tsimshian princess. This, as she soon saw was a halibut fishing camp with hundreds of Haida people —people taller and fairer than the Tsimshian people. She approached, and the head chief, Gitxan, sent slaves to fetch her to him.

When she stood before him, trembling but proud, he scanned her carefully: her rich but bedraggled furs, slim tattooed hands, ear lobes pierced but almost unornamented. His eyes lighted with recognition; and with some plan, it seemed. He spoke, but his words were foreign.

Beside him stood a chieftainess whose thin black eyebrows bristled with hatred. The finbacked Killer Whale glared from her painted cone-hat, from glistening black slate ear and neck pendants, and from a black labret. Her tattooed hands held black sea-otter fur around her stately person. This was Tahl-lee who hated all Tsimshian people.

Churning with fear inside, Da-ul looked straight at Tahl-lee. Then, more hopefully, she gazed at the gentler Gitxan.

He sent for a Tsimshian woman, a captured Tsimshian woman who appeared with cropped slave's hair

and garments of cedar tatters. At sight of Da-ul's tattooed crests, the woman wept with pleasure. Then interpreting for the chief, she poured out his words:

"Chief Gitxan is a kinsman of yours, Princess. He welcomes you as a daughter. He says Prince Temnaq will be your husband, Princess."

Tah-lee's eyes flashed, fierce as the Killer Whale's that glinted from black slate pendants.

Swallowing a fear of her, Da-ul glanced anxiously toward the forbidding chieftainess. Then she whispered to the Tsimshian woman, "I have some girls with me."

"Your maidens are with you, Princess?"

"My little maidens." Quickly Da-ul told her story to the slave who repeated it, in Haida, to the others.

"They, too, will be Chief Gitxan's daughters," the slave informed the princess, "and I will serve his daughters." Her sad face brightened at the thought of having Tsimshian children around her.

Happy with these arrangements, Da-ul sped to the little girls, but they clung to her weasel robes in fear of strangers. As they stood huddled on the beach, Young Eagle flew to a rock beside them.

The princess stroked his faithful head. Then she whispered to him, "Tell them we're safe, Young Eagle." Taking her last ear ornament, she fastened it about his glossy neck. "Tell them we're safe," she whispered again, and watched him climb the air currents. She watched until he disappeared; then, feeling bereft, she sighed. He and her birthright, she feared, were lost to her forever.

"The Eagle will fly again," she heard a kind voice say in halting Tsimshian. She spun about to find a prince beside her, Temnaq, the Raven prince who was to be her husband. He was handsome and tall, and his dark eyes were smiling at her.

"The Eagle will fly again," he reassured her before moving along to join his waiting paddlers in his sea-hunt canoe. His muscles rippled as his craft sped seaward.

Da-ul's eyes brightened with admiration, then softened to a tender glow.

"Cwaw!" A crow voice shattered the shining morning. "Our great prince takes a slave wife!" It was Tahl-lee.

"Slave wife?" asked Da-ul, blinking.

"Yes. A slave . . . plucked off the beach . . . hungry and ragged and dirty."

"Oh!" gasped indignant Da-ul.

"No marriage gifts," Tahl-lee went on. "No ceremonies. No family to make arrangements. Not even ear-ornaments! He marries a slave who lives by serving others' children." She spat to show her scorn, and the small girls cried out, frightened, and clung to the Eagle princess.

"I'm . . . hungry . . . Princess," a small voice ventured, feebly.

"Princess?" scoffed Tahl-lee. "Drifted log! Bedraggled plume from a fallen Eagle!"

"The Eagle will fly again," said Da-ul softly. And

in her gentle heart she made a vow. Some day, a rightful heir would go to Kitsum-galum. And true to the ancient Blood Code, he would wreak vengeance on the Bear Clan.

To strengthen this resolve, Young Eagle returned one day wearing a shameful pendant. It was a carved bone Eagle, hung upside down, and held by the Bear Clan's emblem. Her grandfather had received it, and had passed it along to Da-ul, reminding her of the shame her clan had suffered.

Snatching the shameful thing from Young Eagle's neck, she threw it into the deep sea.

A rightful heir would go to Kitsum-galum.

As the years passed by, out on the Haida islands, Da-ul's loved Kitsum-galum grew misty with time and distance. Yet in her dreams she saw its towering house-poles. And sometimes she seemed to feel Neeswana's stern eyes on her, and to hear his voice again, "You know your duty, Da-ul."

She had six children now: four handsome boys and two lovely daughters. "Eagles without an aerie," she sometimes thought, watching them play about her.

The eldest boy, Hayis, stood tall and straight, his hair screwed up into a shining topknot and his copper skin tattooed with Tsimshian symbols. He was the rightful heir to Eagle honors. He was also the favorite of Young Eagle and of the little girls, now grown and married.

One day Da-ul watched her children playing on

the long white beach near the Haida village. The girls were popping sundried seaweed blisters while the boys snapped long kelp whips, flicking at moonshells in a merry contest. Another boy played with them—Tahl-lee's youngest—until his mother descended like a Thunderbird to stop him.

"Mingling with slaves!" she stormed, snatching his kelp whip from him. Her haughty eyes surveyed Da-ul's lively children. "Foreigners! Slaves!" she scoffed, and she spat to show her loathing. Then, snapping the long kelp whip herself, she laid it on Hayis's shoulders.

"Tahl-lee!" Da-ul cried out. "A prince does not suffer indignities."

"A prince?" sneered Tahl-lee. "A title as empty as the Eagle lodges at Kitsum-galum!"

Da-ul could hardly hide her blazing anger.

"Why did she call us foreigners?" her younger daughter asked when the chieftainess had left them.

"Because you are," her mother answered sadly. "You can be nothing here, nothing but scorned outsiders." She turned to her eldest son, Hayis, "Your rightful hunting grounds . . . your rightful fishing stations . . . your rightful poles and lodges are at Kitsum-galum."

"I know. And I shall go some day to Kitsum-galum!"

"Some day," his mother agreed. That was his fate: to go to Kitsum-galum and die, perhaps, avenging his murdered kinsmen. The ancient Blood Code demanded this vengeance from him. The honor of all the Eagles rested on him.

Another day the children played with pliant strips of seaweed attached to hold-fast-stones. Aiming them at a rocky tidal pool, the children would let the stones fly, streaming their sea-brown tails. Into the pool they would clunk with a splatter. And, at each CLUNK, the children would shriek with laughter.

Watching with narrowed eyes, Tahl-lee picked up a seaweed strip herself, swinging the stone as though she scarcely noticed. Then, suddenly, she made a vicious circle and loosed the stone. It hurtled through the air to strike Prince Hayis.

"Tahl-lee!" gasped Da-ul.

"Mother of foreigners!" scoffed Tahl-lee.

"My children are as noble as your own," said Da-ul, her anger boiling. "Their uncles . . ."

". . . are drifted logs. Their uncles are ghosts, hovering and wailing, and waiting in vain for vengeance."

"They will not wait forever," declared young Hayis, his face darkening.

"Boasts!" taunted Tahl-lee. "Boasts as empty as the Eagle House at Kitsum-galum."

"How dare you speak like that to him?" demanded Da-ul.

"To the son of a slave wife?" the other responded lightly. Then, with a malicious glint, she added, "To the nephew of a slave woman who serves Bear Chief Saxsaxt at Kitsum-galum?"

"Slave woman?" breathed Da-ul. Had there been some word of her little sister? Had Wineeks been captured in that pine thicket? Had she been made a slave in her own tribe? "Has there been word of the Princess Wineeks?"

Tahl-lee just laughed and walked away. She did not answer.

That night Da-ul spoke to her husband, Temnaq. "Your sons must claim their birthright," she told him sadly.

"They must win it before they can claim it," answered Temnaq. And from that day he started the boys' strict training. Mornings, in sun or snow, they swam in the cold salt water; then stood bare on the beach while men whipped them with evergreens until their skins glowed like four rosy sunsets. They paddled canoes and climbed timbered mountains. They fasted and bathed. And sometimes, in the seclusion of lonely islands, they practiced their Tsimshian songs and their ancient royal Eagle dances.

One day when, as four strong youths, they sent their craft slicing through heaving sea swells, Tahl-lee said lightly to their watching mother, "I may take your sons myself as my slave paddlers."

"My sons will captain ships," responded Da-ul.

"Not Haida ships!"

"Not Haida ships," Da-ul agreed, with spirit.

Young Eagle perched beside her and sent a loud clear call out on the storm winds.

"The Eagle will fly again," said Da-ul, firmly.

A few years passed, all too swiftly for gentle Da-ul. Raven Prince Temnaq had ordered a great canoe built, a clipper craft carved with the Tsimshian Eagle. He had hunted sea otter and ordered six handsome robes made. He had hunted sea lion for tough new suits of armor. He had watched over the making of spears and had tested their strength and sharpness. He had also arranged for boxes of bowls, spoons, bracelets, and earrings, all decorated with Tsimshian totems. His people brought food boxes, painted and carved and inlaid, and dried foods to store inside them. They brought patterned mats and paddles carved with the royal emblems. And then, one day, Prince Temnaq gathered his handsome family.

"The time has come," he told them.

"The time has come," said Hayis, his voice vibrant with pride and purpose.

"The time has come," said Da-ul, clutching her daughters to her. "You carry the pride and hope of all the Eagles because a shamed clan cannot prosper." She seemed to hear Neeswana's voice, thundering and unrelenting: "A princess's heart must beat for all her clan, not for herself and her own nearest dear ones." Lifting her trembling chin, she pushed her daughters from her. "The time has come," she told them.

Young Eagle preened himself and oiled his feathers.

"As you must preen yourselves," reminded Da-ul. "Your appearance must fill discouraged hearts with courage." She looked fondly at the bird. "Make a crosspiece for Young Eagle," she said. "I know he will guide my children back to their mother's land."

When all was ready, Da-ul's six children stood before their mother, handsome and straight, shining with health. The girls' braids glistened, decorated with seashells and feathers. The boys' dark skins glowed under their tattooed emblems. Each had a lustrous sea-otter robe: white for the girls, black for the four tall brothers. All wore ear ornaments and glinting carved copper bracelets. And, honoring their princely father, each wore one raven feather.

Four of their father's slaves stepped up with paddles. But Hayis refused. "We have no slaves," he said. He took a paddle, as did each younger brother.

The smaller girl rushed back to cling to Da-ul.

"We could . . . keep . . . one?" Da-ul said to her husband.

"We could keep one," he agreed, his own eyes misted.

And so they went, the five high hearted Eagles: four boys and one lone girl. She had been named Wineeks because they had thought that name was empty.

Da-ul's "maidens," now grown and married watched with their Haida husbands. Their own children would go some day, they knew, across those waters.

The five young Eagles ventured now where they had never been, across strange waters. When they left the Haida village, they paddled for a while with a fair west wind behind them. When the wind strengthened, they flatted their paddle blades to catch the wind and use it. When it veered round, they bent again to their rhythmic stroking.

About them the great sea heaved. Kelp heads bobbed, trailing their sea-brown tresses, and kelp tubes tangled themselves, writhing like brown sea serpents. Fins of swift killer whales sliced through the sea swells, and basking sea lions watched them with bristling whiskers.

With respect the girl Wineeks scattered white eagle down upon the waters. Theirs was a treacherous way, they knew, subject to sudden squalls and blinding fogs and wild storms.

They slept at Root-Basket-Camp, then at Slave Island, Beaver Tail Island, and Hole Island, staying a day each time to rest and fish and to limber their cramped leg muscles.

Then the carved Eagle prow nosed in among blue-and-white snow capped mountains, entering the deep fiord that lies between the ancient homes of the Tlingit and the Tsimshian peoples.

"It is a lovely land," they said, remembering with sinking hearts the great white beaches left behind.

Young Eagle threw back his fierce white head and screamed in regal triumph. Then, spreading his huge dark wings, he mounted the air to soar high, high above them.

"Gone to herald our approach," boasted Prince Hayis gayly. His voice was buoyant, but his eyes were anxious.

"It . . . is a long time since Mother left them," Wineeks remarked, twisting a thick black braid with nervous fingers.

"A long, long time!" Hayis picked up her words and gave them vibrancy. "A long, long time for clansmen to have their proud heads bowed. But we will lift the shame that weighs upon them." Though his voice was strong and sure, his eyes watched with troubled glances, for the eagle's coming.

In two days time, Young Eagle returned to them, screeching with much excitement.

"They are expecting us," guessed Hayis boldly.

As though affirming this, Young Eagle perched high on a bony snag to preen himself and oil his glistening feathers.

"We, too," Hayis reminded his royal crew. "Our appearance must fill discouraged hearts with courage." He leapt into the stream and came out glowing.

It was the Moon of Leafing. The wind was honeyed with the springtime fragrance of opening cottonwood buds; the trees stood golden green against blue mountains.

"Our mother's land and ours," breathed Wineeks softly.

"Our mother's land and ours is Kitsum-galum," her brother corrected her.

At Fishery Bay they found the run was over. The "oolaken trees" were bare, the camp deserted; but the young folk looked about with eager interest. This was the place where their mother had been cast seaward.

They readied themselves to meet their Nishga cousins: they shook out their sea-otter robes, painted red eagle wings on their bronzed handsome faces, and sprinkled white eagle down on their dark hair to show they came in peace along the river. They polished their sleek canoe, then started upstream.

As they neared the Nishga village, they raised their voices in a Tsimshian boat song. And people rushed to the bank, shouting and weeping and waving their arms and paddles. Wineeks, in shining white sea-otter robes, a-glisten with pearly discs of abalone, seemed supernatural. The richly clad princes, trained by a great sea hunter, flourished their paddles in graceful and proud precision, depicting the homeward flight of the mightly Eagle.

High on the prow, Young Eagle spread his wings in regal triumph.

"Bring them to me!" commanded old old Neeswana as slaves carried his shrunken form down to the river bank. Rising up on one bony elbow, he scanned the young faces sternly. He considered their clothes, their bearing. "The Eagle will fly again," he said at last. Then he lay back, dying, his wrinkled old face relaxed with satisfaction.

Away from him, the Nishga Eagles clamored for information. What of Princess Da-ul? What of the long lost children?

"They are all well and married, with children of their own," Prince Hayis told them. "Now, give me word in turn. What of Kitsum-galum?"

Faces grew sad around the royal Eagles. Eyes lowered before their searching eyes. Tongues were silent.

"What of Kitsum-galum?" Hayis demanded of them.

Reluctantly, at last, they answered Hayis.

More than twenty years had passed at Kitsum-galum without one word about the vanished princess, without one word of coming heirs or vengeance.

The towering pride of the Eagle was gone forever. Or so it seemed to Bear Chief Saxsaxt who was about to claim the captured royal emblems. Once he had claimed them, and had had his claim witnessed at a potlatch, the cherished royal crests would be lost to the Eagle people.

Chief Saxsaxt had been waiting long for this time of triumph. Yet now, when it was approaching, he sensed rebellion beneath the outward respect of all his clansmen. They made the potlatch preparations with sullen faces. They seemed daily more irritable.

The Bear Clan people were consumed by their own misgivings.

"No good will come of this," they were muttering to one another. "It was an evil thing to murder our Tsimshian tribesmen."

"An evil thing arranged by wicked Wigad."

They cast fearful glances toward the old witchdoctor. And at night they listened to the wind and heard the wailings of the Eagle ghosts who haunted the empty lodges. The ghosts were drifting in the air, they knew, like lonely logs, as they waited for atonement.

"It was an evil thing to murder our own Tsimshian tribesmen," they kept repeating. It went against nature. It offended too many spirits. And the spirits had shown their anger. Bear Clansmen shivered remembering that, of all the murdering Bear group, only Saxsaxt remained. The others had been mysteriously killed by rockslides, snowslides, and rapids. And the whole Bear Clan had been dogged by a strange misfortune.

"The spirits are angry with us."

"And they will be more angry still when we add insult to murder."

Their eyes filled with rebellious fires when they chanced to light on Wigad.

It had been he who had counselled the massacre in

that long ago hungry winter. And now it was Wigad
who counselled the boastful potlatch. By his advice,
Chief Saxsaxt was finally about to claim the captured
totems. He had ordered them carved on a handsome
pole that lay now before his feastlodge, ready for rais-
ing at a lavish potlatch.

"This will arouse the wrath of Eagle clans all along
the Ksan and the Nass River valleys," people muttered.
"And they are already infuriated by our treatment of
the Princess Wineeks."

Above all other things, the Bear people were uneasy
about the degradation of Da-ul's younger sister. She
had been captured, and made a slave, her proud hair
cropped and her wealthy robes replaced by cedar tatters. For twenty years she had served the Bear Chief,
Saxsaxt.

"A Tsimshian woman should not be made a slave,"
they had muttered all through those twenty years. "It
shames all Tsimshian women."

"And it angers all Tsimshian men, especially all
Tsimshian Eagles."

They turned their eyes away from tragic Wineeks.

"This potlatch is an evil thing," they kept repeating
to one another. Yet they went on with the preparations
for it. They were afraid to draw the wrath of wicked
Wigad. He had the power to cast a spell on them.

So, angry and grudging as they were, they continued the preparations. Witnesses from other tribes had
already been invited; they must be feasted and entertained. They must all be paid by lavish gifts of furs and

cedar mats and finely carved spoons and dishes. Great visiting chiefs must receive canoes, Chilkat mantles, or copper shields, or slaves. So the Bears kept giving things to Chief Saxsaxt. But they gave them with grudging faces.

"This is a foolish potlatch," they muttered darkly. "Evil will come of it." To them it seemed that the wind grew louder and, so also the wailing of ghosts above the Eagle houses.

Then Chief Saxsaxt announced:

"The slave Wineeks will die beneath the new pole."

"Chief Saxsaxt's potlatch will be held after this fall's goat hunt," the Nishga people told the horrified young Eagles.

"That potlatch will never be!" vowed angry Hayis. "Who follows the trail with me to Kitsum-galum?"

As though the very wind spread word of vengeance, Eagle Clan warriors rushed in to the Nishga village. Each one dipped his finger into the sacred box of oil and licked his finger, swearing allegiance to the Eagle heir-presumptive. Then they broke the box and burned it. They painted their faces, took war clubs and spears and armor. And they followed the warpath south to Kitsum-galum.

The faithful eagle followed, flying his own high trail above the tree tops.

When they came to the lovely mirror lake of Kitsum-galum, they found great floats of lily pads glistening with bloom and scudding among them lively duck broods. Along the shore, pale aspens shimmered among dark spruces and among the jackpine. Under the trees were drifts of rose swamp laurel and bright pink shooting stars and yellow violets. Ferns feathered pale green above darker lacy mosses.

"This is a lovely land," whispered gentle young Wineeks.

"This is our land," said her brothers, standing proudly.

That night they crept with stealth into the empty Eagle lodges; they filled the air with ghostly cedar bugles. And they chanted the wild war chant of Eagle princes.

Listening, the Bear clan people shivered with apprehension. They thought this was some ghostly visitation, some long-dreaded spirit revenge on boastful Saxsaxt.

"He should not have made the princess a slave," they muttered, hearing the royal war chant. "He should not have murdered our tribesmen." Fearful of they knew not what, they slipped from their sleeping platforms. Trembling with a dread of supernatural vengeance, they sought the protecting forest.

Only Chief Saxsaxt slept on untroubled by sounds or conscience. Only Wigad stayed close to the flickering lodgefire. They were alone in Bear House.

The elder Wineeks, hearing the war chant, sang paens of silent welcome. These were no ghosts, she knew. That was her family's war chant. These were true heirs, returned to their empty lodges. With pounding heart, she sped toward the Eagle houses. She had advice for attacking Eagles.

Before dawn broke, Prince Hayis and his men entered Bear House. They slew the swaggering Saxsaxt and wily Wigad.

"Now set fire to the pole!" commanded the tall young leader.

This done, with troubled eyes, he looked toward the forest. Like all his race, he hated bloodshed; yet he knew his sacred duty to his murdered clansmen. Their ghosts must all be freed by due atonement.

Peering out of the forest's gloom, Bear clansmen knew that true men, not ghosts, had come. And they had no heart to press this quarrel further. Lamenting the past, they consulted about the future. Perhaps, they said, perhaps the new young chief would let them soothe the ghosts with reparations. Perhaps he would let them wipe out the Eagle shame with payment of all the wealth now collected for Saxsaxt's potlatch.

And so when morning came, their messengers emerged from the trees, scattering white eagle down as they moved forward. The Bears were suing for peace-with-reparations. They would tender the Eagle Feather, the sacred white eagle tail feather that brought back peace and friendship. If the new young Eagle Chief accepted the Eagle Feather, there might be peace again within the tribe that lived at Kitsum-galum.

As was the Indian way, delegates from both clans considered long about it. Councils from both sides talked and planned and argued. For days and nights, wild chants and cedar bugles ripped the air. And people grew weary and tense and apprehensive.

Then the moment came, the fateful moment that brought the opposing chiefs together to offer the Eagle Feather and to accept or to refuse it.

This was the moment that would waft the white eagle down, or raise the blood-red warclubs.

Leaders on both sides donned ancient regalia: carved crestal crowns, handsome patterned Chilkat mantles, and glittering ear ornaments. Chiefs picked up their staffs and their carved bird rattles.

Now there would be peace—or war—at Kitsum-galum. People fell silent. The drums were hushed. The very trees seemed to still themselves to listen.

Every eye was on young Prince Hayis. He held the fate of all in his slim strong fingers.

He advanced toward Saxsaxt's heir in royal Eagle raiment that had been stored for twenty years in painted cedar boxes. Beside him, his slender sister moved in shining white sea-otter robes a-glisten with pearly discs of abalone. Her beauty and grace stirred a ripple of admiration.

Saxsaxt's heir, a handsome young Bear Clan noble, tore his wistful gaze from her to fix his dark eyes on her solemn brother. "Here is the Feather of Friend-ship," he said in a voice deep with respect and humble with wrongs admitted. He held aloft a pure white eagle tail feather. "Let our outrage be forgiven!" he entreated. "We will atone for it. We will fill your arms with treasures. Prince, Eagle Chief, let our outrage be forgiven! Let the sun shine again on Kitsum-galum!

Let friendship be restored within the tribe!" He shook
his head to let clouds of white eagle down waft from
the encircling sea-lion bristles. Then he tendered the
Eagle Feather.

The gathered clans stood silent, Eagles, Bears,
Wolves, and Ravens: all held their breath for one

tense waiting moment.

Would there be peace—or war—at Kitsum-galum?

The eyes of all were fixed on young Prince Hayis.

He raised his staff, and Princess Wineeks inclined her shining head to let the young Bear leader plant the white Eagle Feather above her raven braids.

Then joy burst forth. Drums throbbed. People beat on boards. Singing maidens chanted.

The sun would shine again on Kitsum-galum.

But before he could be Eagle Chief, Hayis must make his claim to the ancient title. And his claim must be duly witnessed. So he must give a potlatch, awarding the gifts the Bear Clan had provided, and adding more gifts from the happy Eagle peoples. Since they would be returned, some day, these gifts would insure his fortune.

But first, before all else, there must be a message to Princess Da-ul.

"Tell her we're safe, Young Eagle," Prince Hayis whispered. He took a tiny pouch of eagle down and dropped in six glistening trinkets—one from each prince and princess, including the elder Wineeks. "Tell her we're safe, Young Eagle," he repeated, tying the pouch around the faithful bird's neck feathers.

Young Eagle spread his wings above the forest.

Da-ul was on the beach when the eagle reached her, on the long white beach that fronted her Haida village. Seeing the trinkets and eagle down, she wept with joy and stroked Young Eagle fondly. Then she gazed across the sea toward Kitsum-galum.